CW00384518

AN INTRODUCTION TO
PROTOCHORDATA

AN
INTRODUCTION TO
PROTOCHORDATA

By
H.S. Bhamrah
Kavita Juneja

Edited by
Balvinder K.

ANMOL PUBLICATIONS PVT. LTD.
NEW DELHI - 110 002 (INDIA)

ANMOL PUBLICATIONS PVT. LTD.

4374/4B, Ansari Road, Daryaganj
New Delhi - 110 002

An Introduction to Protochordata
© Authors
First Edition, 1990
Reprint, 1991, 1992, 1994
Second Revised Edition, 2002
ISBN 81-261-0709-X

[All rights reserved. No part of this publication may be reproduced, stored in a retrieval system or transmitted, in any form or by any means, mechanical, photocopying, recording or otherwise, without prior written permission of the publisher.]

PRINTED IN INDIA

Published by J.L. Kumar for Anmol Publications Pvt. Ltd., New Delhi - 110 002 and Printed at Mehra Offset Press, Delhi.

Contents

Contents

Preface

We feel pleasure in bringing out the second revised edition of the present book on the instance of our learned teachers. Besides rectifying the errors of first edition, new material is added here and there in the light of recent development and researches in the field.

This text is designed to approach the morphology, anatomy, physiology and development of the *Protochordata* in a coherent way since it is most natural for a student in studying the architectural elements of an animal body in the quest to know how they function. This text intends, therefore, to enable the student, through his own natural appetency, to correlate form and function so that he possesses for subsequent work in either anatomy or physiology a firm foundation for a real edifice of knowledge.

The book features both a text and a laboratory guide. It deals with the structures and physiological phenomena of each system. Origin, adaptative radiation and other general topics are also dealt in details. It is hoped that this book will not only meet the requirement of Indian students but will also be useful as a guideline to the teachers in their teaching.

There can be no claim to originality except in the manner of treatment and much of the information has been obtained from the books and scientific journals available in different libraries.

We express our thanks to our friends and colleagues whose constant inspiration have initiated them to bring out this book.

The authors are also grateful to Dr. J. Bahadur, Professor and Head, School of Studies in Zoology, Jiwaji University Gwalior, Dr. A.K. Pandey, Professor & Head, Vikram University, Ujjain for their valuable suggestions.

All the constructive criticisms and suggestions for improvement from learned teachers and scholars are welcome.

H.S. Bhamrah
Kavita Juneja

Hemichordata : Characters & Classification

Hemichordata was previously known as *Enteropneusta* a name given by *Gegenbaur* (1870) due to the presence of gill-slits in *Balanoglossus clavigerus. Bateson* (1885) suggested the name Hemichordata in place of Enteropneusta. He noted many features of structures and development which these animals share with lower chordates like Cephalochordata and Urochordata. Although this name has been universally accepted but its systemic position remained controversial. Its Chordata status is very much in question now-a-days and hence it is considered as separate phylum of Invertebrata by *Hyman* (1959).

Characters

1. The hemichordates are solitary or colonial mostly tubicolous, soft and fragile animals.
2. Body is divisible into the proboscis, collar and trunk.
3. They are vermiform, unsegmented, bilaterally symmetrical and triploblastic.
4. The appendages are absent. In some the collar may bear arms with tentacles.
5. Body wall with single layered epidermis. Dermis is absent.
6. Coelom is enterocoelous divisible into *protocoel* or *proboscis coelom*, *mesocoel* or *collar coelom* and *metacoel* or *trunk coelom*.
7. Buccal diverticulum, wrongly named as notochord, is present.
8. Alimentary canal is complete, in the form of a straight or 'U' shaped tube.
9. Respiration by gill-slits, one to several pairs are present. One pair in *Cephalodiscus*, several in *Balanoglossus* and absent in *Rhabdopleura*.
10. Circulatory system is open type with a central sinus, heart vesicle, dorsal and ventral vessels, sinuses and lateral vessels.
11. Excretion is performed by the glomerulus present in proboscis coelom and connected with blood vessels.

12. Nervous system is primitive comprising mainly of an intra-epidermal nerve plexus.
13. Mode of reproduction is sexual but some of them also exhibit asexual reproduction.
14. Development may be direct i.e. without larval stage or indirect i.e. with a *Tornaria larva.*
15. The hemichordates are exclusively marine and all feed on micro-organisms and debris by ciliary mechanism. There are about 70 species.

CLASSIFICATION

Phylum. Hemichordata is divided into following classes :

(1) Enteropneusta, (2) Pterobranchia (3) Plactosphaeroidea and (4) Graptolita (Extinct)

Class - 1. Enteropneusta

1. They are free, solitary, burrowing animals, commonly known as '*Acorn*' or '*Tongue worms*'.
2. Body is divisible into proboscis, collar and trunk. Proboscis tapers anteriorly, collar without tentaculate arms.
3. Alimentary canal is straight tube having two rows of hepatic caecae in the intestinal region.
4. Several pairs of gill-slits.
5. Sexes are separate, gonads are numerous and sac-like.
6. Development is indirect through the *Tornaria larval* stage.

   Examples : *Balanoglossus, Saccoglossus.*

Class-2. Pterobranchia

1. These are sedentary, colonial and tubicolous animals.
2. Body is very short and vase-like. Proboscis is shield shaped and the collar with hollow, ciliated arms bearing tentacles.
3. Gill-slits one pair or absent, if present it is never 'U' shaped.
4. The alimentary canal is 'U' shaped with anus near the mouth.
5. Bisexual or unisexual: one pair of gonad or one gonad. Asexual reproduction by budding.
6. Development may be direct or indirect.

   Class -Pterobranchia is divided into two orders:

Order (i) Rhabdopleurida

1. Collar with two tentaculated arms.
2. Gill-slits are absent.

3. Single gonad is found.
4. They are colonial; individuals of the colony are connected by a stolon.
   Example : *Rhabdopleura.*

Order (ii) Cephalodiscida

1. They are solitary but are enclosed in a common gelatinous case.
2. Collar with several tentaculated arms.
3. One pair of gill-silts is present.
4. One pair of gonads is present.
   Example : *Cephalodiscus.*

Class-3. Planctosphaeroidea

1. This class is represented by pelagic and transparent larvae.
2. Body is spherical with branched ciliated bands on the surface.
3. The alimentary canal is 'L'shaped.
4. A triangular protocoel opening out side by a hydropore. Paired mesocoel and metacoel are also present.
   Example : *Planctosphaera.*

SACCOGLOSSUS

Phylum	-	Hemichordata
Class	-	Enteropneusta
Genus	-	*Saccolossus*

1. It is commonly known as *'Tongue worm'* of North America.
2. It is worm-like and the body is divisible into proboscis, collar and trunk.
3. It is a marine and tubicolous animal, living in semitransparent tunnel with mucous secretion. It feeds on planktons.
4. The proboscis is much longer and the trunk is irregularly ringed superficially.
5. Collar posteriorly overhangs the trunk so as to cover 3 or 4 gill-slits.
6. Trunk is differentiated into three regions, an anterior having numerous pairs of gill-slits; middle has gonads (grey in female and yellow in male). Posterior region has intestine and bears an anus.
7. Genital wings, hepatic caeca, synapticula and nerve roots are absent.
8. Development is direct without larval stage.
9. It is found in New Zealand, Australia, North America etc.

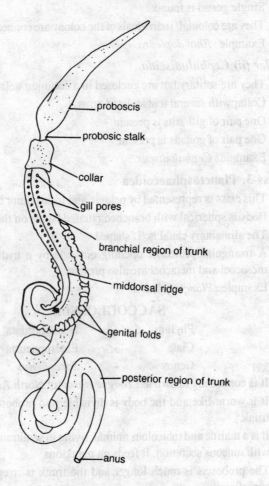

Fig. 12.1. *Saccoglossus.*

RHABDOPLEURA

Phylum	-	Hemichordata
Class	-	Pterobranchia
Order	-	Rhabdopleurida
Genus	-	*Rhabdopleura*

1. It is a marine and colonial hemichordate.
2. The colony consists of horizontal branching gelatinous tubes forming the *coenoecium* which is secreted and formed by the animal.

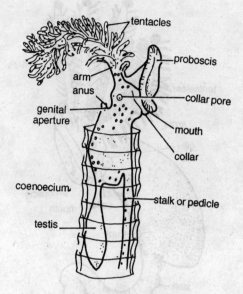

Fig. 12.2. *Rhabdopleura.*

3. Each individual or zooid is composed of a stalk or pedicle, trunk sac, oral lamella, pigment stripe, cephalic shield, arms and tentacles.

4. Collar bears a pair of hollow elongated arms beset with numerous fine ciliated tentacles for food collection.

5. Alimentary canal is 'U' shaped, anus is near the mouth.

6. Gill-slits and glomerulus are absent.

7. Sexes are separate but a colony has both the male and female individuals.

8. A single gonad is present on the right side of trunk.

9. Development is indirect.

10. Asexual reproduction by budding.

11. It is mainly found in Norway and Ireland coasts.

CEPHALODISCUS

Phylum	-	Hemichordata
Class	-	Pterobranchia
Order	-	Cephalodiscida
Genus	-	*Cephalodiscus*

1. It is a marine colonial animal.

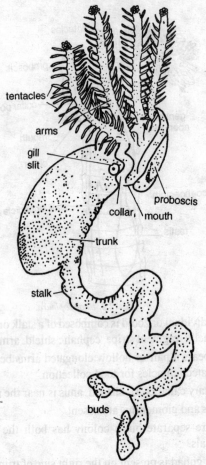

Fig. 12.3. *Cephalodiscus.*

2. It is sedentary and gregarious animal found mainly in the seas of Southern Hemisphere.

3. The colony consists of several unconnected animals or zooids which are enclosed in a common case known as *coenoecium*.

4. Each zooid is 2-3 mm long and is divisible into proboscis. collar and trunk.

5. The proboscis is shield shaped overhanging the mouth. The protocoel opens out through two proboscis pores.

6. Collar has 8-16 hollow arms or lophophores. The arms possess heavily ciliated tentacles used for food capture.

7. Trunk is short divisible into two parts, anterior part contains alimentary canal and gonads while posterior part is slender adhesive stalk.

8. Alimentary canal is 'U' shaped. A single pair of gill-slit is present without skeletal support.

9. Sexes are separate. Development is direct.

10. Asexual reproduction takes place by budding. The bud arises from stalk and soon becomes free.

BALANOGLOSSUS

Phylum	-	Hemichordata
Class	-	Enteropneusta
Genus	-	*Balanoglossus*

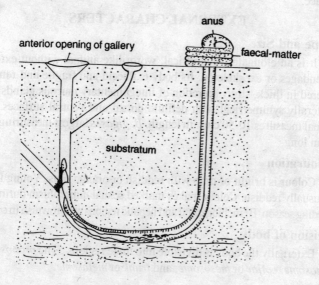

Fig. 12.4. Balanoglossus in its burrow.

Habits and Habitat

Balanoglossus usually lives in burrowing condition but some times it may be seen under the stones. rocks etc. It has a world-wide distribution. It is marine and chiefly found in shallow, intertidal waters along the warm and temperate oceans. These animals burrow in the sandy mud and secrete the integumentary mucous to cement the sand grains. The burrow is usually 'U' shaped. It has two openings. the anterior opening is large and funnel shaped while the posterior opening is small and circular and concealed below the spirally coiled faecal matter of the animal. The faecal coil resembles the castings of earthworms. The anterior opening may give out side branches.

Balanoglossus feeds on planktons and organic debris. It is a sluggish and inactive creature and moves about slowly with the aid of cilia which are present on the greater part of the body. Sexes are separate and the development is through larval stage known as *tornaria larva*. Asexual reproduction is absent but power of regeneration is well marked.

About 20 species of *Balanoglossus* are present all over the world, a few of them are *B. australiensis, B. carnosus, B. jamaicensis, B. gigas, B.misakiensis* etc. *B. misakiensis* and allied genera emit bright greenish luminescence emanating from a slimy substance discharged from body surface.

EXTERNAL CHARACTERS

Shape and Size

It is an elongated, cylindrical, worm-like animal without external appendages or exoskeleton. Its body is flaccid and fragile and remains covered in thick, slimy secretion of integumentary mucous glands. It is bilaterally symmetrical with definite dorsal and ventral surfaces. The animal measures 10-50 cms. in length. *B. gigas* is largest measuring over 1.5 m long.

Colouration

Colour is bright or drab with reddish or orange tints. Young forms are usually reddish. Colour makes marked sexual dimorphism during the breeding season. Branchiogenital and hepatic regions are brownish in colour.

Division of body

Externally the body is divisible into three regions : The *proboscis* or *protosome*. *collar* or *mesosome*, and *trunk* or *metasome*.

Proboscis

It is the anterior-most part of the body and is conical in form, tapering anteriorly. Posteriorly, it continues into a narrowed proboscis stalk which is mostly concealed under the collar and is continuous with the inner surface of the dorsal wall of collar. Below the stalk base the proboscis bears a 'U' shaped ciliated depression called the *preoral ciliary organ* which is a *chemoreceptor*. Proboscis encloses *protocoel* or coelom of proboscis. The proboscis coelom opens out through the *proboscis pore* situated mid-dorsally near its base.

Collar

It is the middle, short and thick belt-like part of body, lying behind the proboscis. Its surface is often marked with circular grooves or elevations. The anterior funnel-like part of collar that encircling the proboscis stalk is called *collarette*. Ventrally, below the proboscis stalk, the collarette encloses a wide aperture, the *mouth*. The collar is well demarcated from the trunk behind by a circular constriction. The collar has thick musculature and encloses the *collar coelom*. Sometimes the collar coelom is divided into left and right parts by drosal and ventral mesenteries. The collar coelom opens by a pair of collar pores into the first pair of branchial sacs.

Trunk

It is the posterior and largest part of the body. It is somewhat flattened and usually shows superficial annulations. It is also marked by mid-dorsal

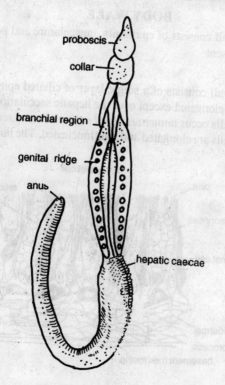

Fig. 12.5. *Balanoglossus*. External features.

and mid-ventral longitudinal ridges. It is differentiated into three regions: the anterior *branchio-genital region*, middle *hepatic region* and posterior *abdominal region*. The branchio-genital region is distinguished by the presence of a longitudinal row of gill-pores on either side of mid-dorsal ridge. Each row of gill-pores is mounted on a prominant ridge-like elevation. The sides of branchio-genital region are thin and leaf-like and are referred to as *genital wings*, containing the gonads. The gonads open out through gonopores which are microscopic apertures. The genital wings are usually curved and folded as the dorsal side coming close together in the median line thereby concealing the gill-pores.

The hepatic region is marked by numerous small, paired, transverse folds, the *hepatic caeca*, on the dorsal side. It is dark brownish or greenish in colour.

The post-hepatic region or abdominal region gradually tapers behind and bears a terminal anus.

BODY WALL

The body wall consists of epidermis, musculature and peritoneum. The dermis is absent.

1. Body wall

The Body wall consists of a single layer of ciliated epithelial cells which are much elongated except over the hepatic sacculations. Among the epidermal cells occur numerous *gland cells* and some *sensory cells*. The epithelial cells are elongated and multinucleated. The nuclei usually

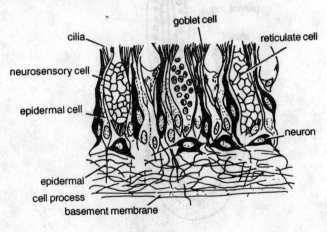

Fig. 12.6. *Balanoglossus*. T.S. of body wall.

lie near the swollen base. The cytoplasm is uniform. At the outer margin numerous cilia are present. Each cilium emerges out from a basal granule. All the basal granules are connected with rhizoplast or neurosome. These cilia move in metachronal rhythm.

Three types of gland cells are present, which are given below :

(i) *Mulberry cells.* These are filled with coarse cytoplasmic granules which are grouped in such a way that it looks like mulberry. They secrete amylase.

(ii) *Reticulate gland cells.* These cells contain large number of vacuoles. The cytoplasm is in a very small quantity. These cells secrete mucous that spreads over the body surface.

(iii) *Goblet cells.* Each cell is with a large flask shaped expansion and a slender proximal stalk. The nucleus is present in the swollen part. Each cell gives rise slender cytoplasmic stalk which tapers towards the base.

The gland cells are numerous in the collar region. Besides, neurosensory cells are present in the epidermis of proboscis and anterior part of collar. These cells take dark stain. Posteriorly the fibres of these cells synapse with tripolar or quadripolar nerve cells which are present in the mesh-work.

Below the epidermal cells is a thick *nervous layer* consisting of a network of nerve cells and fibres. Below the nervous layer is a thick *basement membrane* which supports the epidermis. The basement membrane has a special significance, because it gives rise to the proboscis skeleton.

2. Musculature

The musculature is poorly developed. The muscles are smooth and characterstically arise from coelomic epithelium, therefore, they mostly tend to occupy the coelomic space. In the proboscis an outer layer of circular muscle fibres and inner layer of longitudinal muscle fibres are present. In the trunk region only the longitudinal muscle fibres are present.

3. Peritoneum

It covers the muscles internally, lining the coelom.

Functions of Body Wall

1. It protects the internal organs from injury.
2. Mucous, secreted by gland cells, adheres the sand particles for lining the burrow in which the animal lives.
3. Sensory cells receive external stimuli.
4. Musculature brings about the movement.

Coelom

Early developmental stages of *Balanoglossus* possess a spacious coelom lined with peritoneum. It is *enterocoelous* in origin. As the adult condition is attained, the coelomic epithelium gives rise to the connective tissue and muscle fibres. Hence the coelomic cavity is obliterated. The coelom as a whole is divided into three parts. These include one cavity in proboscis, the *protocoel;* two in collar, the *mesocoel;* and and two in trunk the *metacoel.*

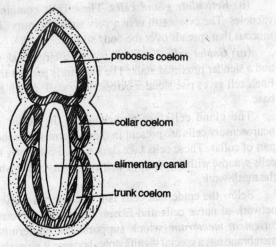

Fig. 12.7. *Balanoglossus.* Embryonic representation of coelom.

(i) Protocoel

In the proboscis, the coelom is a small, unpaired cavity into which several structures like buccal diverticulum, central sinus, heart vesicle, glomerulus etc. project from the base of the proboscis. The proboscis coelom opens out through a dorsal pore at the base of proboscis.

(ii) Mesocoel

In the collar the coelom consists of two separate sac-like cavities on left and right side due to the presence of dorsal and ventral mesenteries. They communicate with the first pair of gill-sac by a pair of collar pores.

(iii) Metacoel

In the trunk the coelom consists of a pair of cavities which are separated by an incomplete mid-dorsal and complete ventral mesenteries. The trunk coelom is filled with coelomic fluid containing amoeboid corpuscles. the *coelomocytes.* They originated from coelomic epithelium.

According to *Spengel* (1893), the coelomocytes secrete a membrane around any foreign particle which invade the animal thus behaving like leucocytes.

Endoskeleton

A definite endoskeletal system is absent in *Balanoglossus* but the basement membrane becomes extra-ordinarily thickened and lamellated to perform the function of skeleton. Following are the skeletal elements.

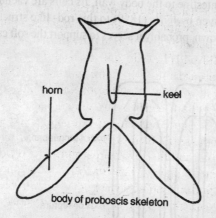

Fig. 12.8. *Balanoglossus*. Proboscis skeleton.

1. Proboscis skeleton

It is a 'Y' shaped structure, partly secreted by the epithelium and partly by coelomic tissue. It resembles to a hyoid apparatus in general appearance. It consists of a *median plate* in the proboscis stalk continued behind into two narrow horns which extend into the roof of buccal cavity. The median plate produced ventrally into The median plate lies below the buccal diverticulum.

2. Buccal diverticulum

It is short, hollow and stiff tube-like projection extends forward through the proboscis stalk into the proboscis coelom. *Bateson* (1885) referred to it as alleged notochord. It is termed as *stomochord* by *Willy* (1899) and *Dawydoff* (1948). *Hyman* preferred to call it as the buccal diverticulum. Its wall is composed of a single layer of tall, slender, vacuolated endodermal cells. *Silen* (1950) has concluded it as an extension of the preoral-region of the digestive tract.

3. Branchial Skeleton

It is also formed by the thickening of basement membrane. The pharynx is perforated with 'U' shaped gill- slits are supported by thickening of pharyngeal epithelium. Branchial skeleton is a trifid structure and it consists of numerous 'M' shaped chitinous rods. Its median bar is situated in the septum and the lateral bars traverse in the tongue bars of adjacent gill-slits. Only the median bar bifurcated ventrally.

4. Pygochord

It is a mid-ventral longitudinal band of the cells extending backwards from the wall of intestine to the body wall. Its cells are vacuolated. Term pygochord was given by *Willy* (1899) to this rod- like structure. Its true function is not known, probably it serves to support the soft caudal region of the trunk.

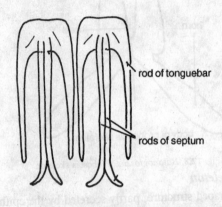

rod of tonguebar

rods of septum

Fig. 12.9. *Balanoglossus.* Branchial skeleton.

DIGESTIVE SYSTEM

The alimentary canal is a straight tube which starts from mouth and terminates into the anus. It is ciliated and is supported by dorsal and ventral mesenteries. The alimentary canal comprises. mouth. buccal cavity. pharynx, oesophagus, intestine and anus.

Mouth

The mouth is a large circular opening situated on the ventral surface of the base of proboscis stalk and collarette. Previously it was supposed to be permanently open but according to *Knight Johnes* (1952) it can be closed or opened. Its opening is regulated by two sets of muscles. the *radial muscle fibres* open it and the *concentric muscle fibres* close it. The mouth leads into the buccal cavity.

Buccal cavity

It is a short, anterior-most part of the alimentary canal which lies in the collar region and extends back upto the collar-trunk septum. It is lined with tall, vacuolated and ciliated cells. Anteriorly, its roof extends as a short, stiff and hollow inpushing which is termed as the *buccal diverticulum*. Buccal diverticulum projects into the proboscis coelom. A few goblet cells are also present in the lining of buccal cavity.

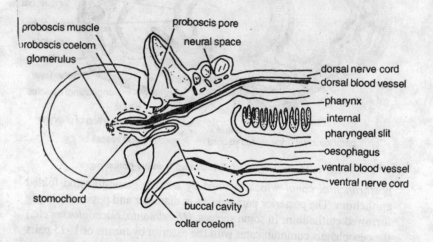

Fig. 12.10. *Balanoglossus*. M.I.S. to show the alimentary canal.

Pharynx

Behind the collar-trunk septum, the buccal cavity leads into the pharynx. The pharynx is differentiated into two parts: the dorsal as *branchial part* bearing gill-slits for respiration and the ventral as *digestive part*. The branchial and digestive parts are demarcated by the presence of lateral longitudinal constrictions called *parabranchial ridges* consisting of tall columnar cells. The branchial part is perforated dorso-laterally by two rows of 'U' shaped ciliated apertures called, *gill-slits* or branchial *apertures*. These slits develop as outgrowth of the pharyngeal wall. In an adult worm their number may be from 40-50 pairs. The digestive part is unperforated and bears ciliated epithelium and gland cells.

Oesophagus

It lies immediately behind the last gill-slit. In *Balanoglossus*, the differentiation of dorsal and ventral parts of pharynx continues for a short distance into the oesophagus. In the oesophagus, the dorsal part is called

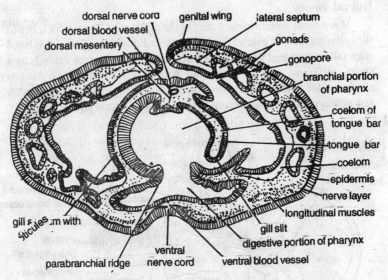

Fig. 12.11. *Balanoglossus.* T.S. through branchio-genital region.

postbranchial canal which is lined by a thick glandular and folded epithelium. The posterior part reduces in diameter and possesses deeply furrowed epithelium. In some species, (*Harrimania, Saccoglossus* etc.) the oesophagus communicates with the exterior by means of 1 -15 pairs of minute oesophageal openings out by dorsally situated minute pores. The oesophageal canals are present in the posterior part of oesophagus and are supposed to be remnants of gill-slits

Intestine

It is the longest part of the alimentary canal. It is distinguishable into anterior *hepatic region* and posterior *post-hepatic region.* The dorsal wall of the hepatic region is thrown into numerous prominent outgrowths called *hepatic caeca.* The hepatic region is richly supplied with blood. Histologically, it shows the presence of many epithelial gland cells containing green or brown inclusions. This region cannot be called as hepatic because it does not show any homology with the liver of vertebrates.

The post-hepatic part runs straight upto anus. It has wide lumen. It is lined with ciliated epithelium. Its walls are provided with numerous sinuses filled with blood. Dorso-laterally. the intestine shows the presence of two well-developed ciliated grooves. sunken in the depressions symmetrically on both the sides. The hinder-most part of the intestine provided with a

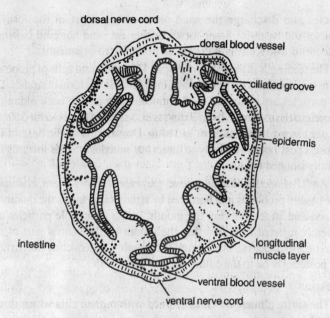

Fig. 12.12. *Balanoglossus.* T.S. through the intestine.

stiff *pygochord*, which is connected with ventral body wall. In *Harrimania*, the last part of intestine is distinguished as a short rectum. The anus is the last part of alimentary canal provided with anal sphincter.

Feeding mechanism

The feeding mechanism of *Balanoglossus* is based on the studies of *Barrington* (1940) and *Knight Johnes* (1953). It feeds on sand particles along with organic food particles through the mouth. It digests the organic

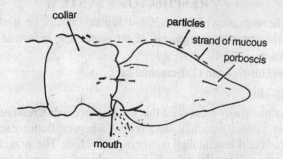

Fig. 12.13. *Balanoglossus.* Feeding current.

particles and discharge the sand out from the anus in the form of characteristic *castings*. Some forms neither eat sand nor emit castings. These forms also feed on diatoms and other micro-organisms.

The feeding is of *muco-ciliary type*. The epidermal cells of proboscis secrete large amounts of the mucous which flows in the form of strands. The food particles are entangled in the mucous and passed back along the proboscis to the collarette. The feeding is also assisted by powerful currents of water caused by the cilia of gill-slits. Dorsal cilia at the base of the proboscis beat latero-ventrally to direct the mucous strands towards the ventrally situated mouth.

An 'U' shaped epidermal groove, the *preoral ciliary organ*, is situated at the base of proboscis and bordered by strong cilia, tastes the quality of the food and water entering the mouth. Large unsuitable particles are efficiently rejected from entering the mouth by the ventral part of the collarette which does so by covering the mouth. Consequently the particle slips posteriorly on to the collar, back of the mouth.

Digestion

The entire alimentary canal is lined with minute cilia which direct the food laden mucous cord backward. The physiology of digestion is poorly known. *Barrington* (1904), reported that the slime of proboscis contains potent *amylase* which probably helps in digestion of glycogen. According to him the cells of hepatic caeca secrete *amylase, maltase,* a weak *protease* and *lipase*, thus proteins, fats and carbohydrates, all, are digested. *Knight Johnes* has claimed that peristalsis occur in the proximal part of oesophagus.

The undigested waste is removed in the form of castings which are in the form of coils round the anal aperture of the burrow.

RESPIRATORY SYSTEM

The respiration in *Balanoglossus* is purely aquatic i.e. it takes oxygen from the water by the process of diffusion. The branchial apparatus comprises:

(1) Gill-slits and (2) Branchial sacs.

1. Gill-slits

As previously mentioned that the pharynx is differentiated into two regions. a dorsal branchial and a ventral digestive. Both are separated by the two lateral longitudinal parabranchial ridges. The branchial part is perforated on dorso-lateral sides by a number of 'U' shaped openings. the gill-slits. Their number varies and increases as the worm grows older.

Actually, in the beginning, the gill-slits are broad and oval and are separated from one another by solid gill-septa. Later, a hollow projection of dorsal pharyngeal wall grows into the slit making 'U' shaped. This projection is called *tongue-bar*. The tongue-bar is hollow and encloses the coelomic cavity. It never touches the ventral side of the gill-slit. A tongue-bar is connected with adjacent gill-septa by short transverse bar called *synapticula*. The gill-septa and tongue bars are ciliated on the pharyngeal faces and are supported by 'M' shaped chitinous rods as described earlier. The cilia on the pharyngeal surface are called *frontal cilia* and along the lateral side are termed *lateral cilia*.

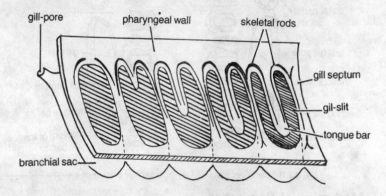

Fig. 12.14. *Balanoglossus*. Development of tongue bar.

2. Branchial sacs

The gill-slits do not open directly on the surface of the body but they first open into a branchial sac which opens out through a *branchial pore*.

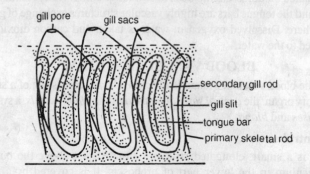

Fig. 12.15. *Balanoglossus*. Gill-slit and branchial sac.

Usually one gill-slit opens into one branchial sac but sometimes their
number increase upto four. The number of branchial pores vary in the
same worm according to age. The branchial sac is lined with cuboidal
cells. The collar coelom communicates with the branchial sac of its side
through collar canal.

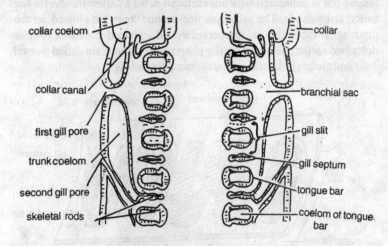

Fig. 12.16. *Balanoglossus*. H.L.S. of branchial portion of pharynx.

Mechanism of Respiration

The lateral cilia of gill-slits by constant beating maintain a regular
respiratory cum food water current. The water current enters the pharynx
via mouth and buccal cavity and goes into the branchial sacs through the
gill-slits. From branchial sacs it goes out through branchial pores which
are situated on dorso-lateral sides in two longitudinal rows. As the gill-
septa and the tongue bars are highly vascular structures exchange of gases
occur here. Dissolved oxygen in water is taken and carbon dioxide is
returned to the water.

BLOOD VASCULAR SYSTEM

The blood vascular system is of *'closed'* type, consisting of a small
pulsatory organ, the *central sinus* or *heart*, definite *blood vessels*, a system
of *sinuses* and *blood*.

1. Central sinus

It is a small, elongated structure situated just above the buccal
diverticulum in the lower part of proboscis. It is covered by a thin
contractile fluid filled sac, the *heart vesicle* or *cardiac-sac*. The heart

vesicle contains muscle fibres in its ventral wall. It contracts rhythmically, assisting the circulation of blood. From the central sinus, the blood directly passes into the glomerulus, where nitrogenous waste products are removed from blood.

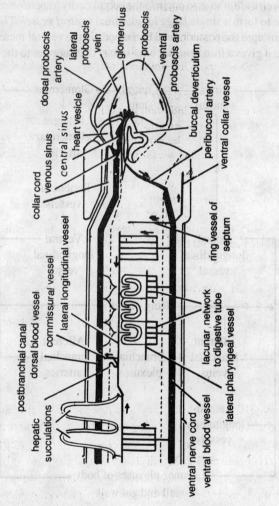

Fig. 12.17a. *Balanoglossus*. Blood vascular system.

2. Blood vessels and sinuses

Four arterial vessels take the blood from the glomerulus. Two of then runs forward into the proboscis and two backwards into the rest of the body. Of the former, one is *mid-dorsal proboscis artery* and other is *mid-ventral proboscis artery*. They supply blood to the dorsal and ventral wall of proboscis. Remaining two are called *efferent glomerular arteries*. The efferent glomerular arteries run backwards, one on either side of buccal diverticulum so as to encircle the buccal cavity as *peribuccal vessels* and unite to form a single large longitudinal *ventral vessel*. The ventral vessel runs upto the posterior end of the body in the ventral mesentery. In its course it gives a thin *ventral collar vessel* that supplies to the collar. It

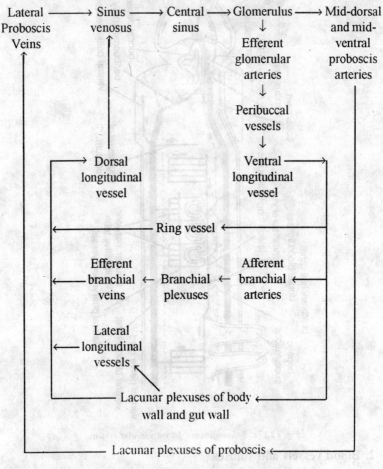

Fig. 12.17(b). Showing course of blood circulation.

gives a *ring-vessel* in collar-trunk septum. From the ring-vessel two lacunar networks are originated, one in the body wall and other in the buccal cavity. The ventral vessel gives out an *afferent branchial artery* to each gill-septum in which it bifurcates to supply two adjacent tongue-bars. All along its length, the ventral vessel supplies the body wall and gut wall by an elaborate network of sinuses.

The *dorsal vessel* is also a longitudinal vessel running within the dorsal mesentery. It starts near the anus and during its forward course it receives blood from body wall, gut wall etc. In the branchial region it receives blood by *efferent branchial veins*. Each efferent branchial vein lies in the tongue bar. At the anterior end of collar, the dorsal vessel dilates to form the *sinus venosus*. Sinus venosus receives a *lateral proboscis vein* from each side of proboscis, then it narrows and opens into the central sinus.

In some forms, a *lateral longitudinal vessel* takes its origin from the subepidermal plexuses in branchial region and runs obliquely backwards, in the intestine it forms a network.

The dorsal and ventral vessels are contractile in nature, consisting of an endothelium and a muscular coat. Blood flows backwards in ventral vessel and forwards in dorsal vessel. The central sinus lacks musculature, therefore, it is non-contractile in nature. The heart vesicle in contractile.

3. Blood

The blood is colourless and contains few cells which are probably detached endothelial cells.

EXCRETORY SYSTEM

The excretory organ is *glomerulus* or *proboscis gland* lying infront of central sinus and projecting into the proboscis coelom. *Bateson* (1885), *Koehler* (1886) and *Schimkewitsch* (1888) accepted its excretory function. The name glomerulus is given by *Spengel* (1893) because it resembles with the glomerulus of vertebrate kidney. It is made up of several tubular projections formed by the peritoneum that covers the buccal diverticulum, central sinus and heart vesicle. The peritoneal cells become cuboidal, columnar or conical in glomerulus. These cells are pale with little amount of cytoplasm. They may contain brown inclusions. From glomerulus the excretory substances pass on into the proboscis coelom and finally to the exterior through the proboscis pore.

NERVOUS SYSTEM

The nervous system is purely of intra-epidermal and primitive type. It consists of a plexus of nerve-cells and nerve-fibres situated in the deeper part of the epidermis outside the basement membrane all over the body. In the network there are bipolar and multipolar nerve cells. Along the mid-dorsal and mid-ventral lines of the nerve net is thickened to form a *dorsal* and *ventral nerve cords*. The two nerve cords are connected by a *circum-enteric nerve ring* at the junction of collar and the trunk. The ventral nerve cord ends at the collar-trunk septum. The dorsal nerve cord extends upto the base of proboscis where it is connected with another circular strand called *anterior nerve ring*. In the collar the dorsal nerve cords become free from the epidermis, lying in the collar coelom above the buccal cavity. This part is known as *collar cord*. The collar cord is hollow and encloses a cavity, the *neurocoel*. The collar cord presumably represents the nervous center but lacks the usual characteristics of the brain. *Spengel* (1893) discovered the presence of the *giant cells*. The number of giant cells vary from 10 - 160 in different species. The giant cells give their fibres in the dorsal and ventral nerve cords. The giant cells were also observed by *Hess* (1937), *Bullock* (1944), *Solen* (1950) and *Knight Johnes* (1952).

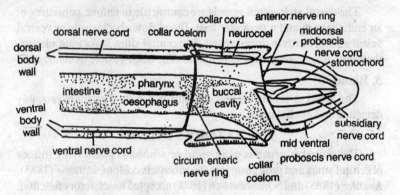

Fig. 12.18. *Balanoglossus.* Nervous system.

SENSE ORGANS

Sense organs of *Balanoglossus* are simple and consist of :

1. Neurosensory cells. The entire body wall is provided with large number of neurosensory cells (*Bullock*, 1945). Each nerve cell is innervated with nerve fibre and has a long sensitive fibre. Their number is higher in proboscis.

2. Pre-oral ciliary organ. It is a 'U' shaped depression bounded by an epidermal ridge. It was discovered by *Brambell* and *Cole* and is composed of tall cells with long cilia. In the centre of this organ the proboscis stalk is present. It tests the quality of food and water hence it is a chemoreceptor.

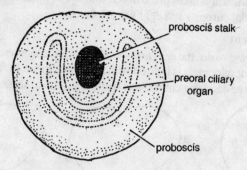

Fig. 12.19. *Balanoglossus*. Pre-oral ciliary organ.

3. Photoreceptor. *Hess* (1938) reported about the specialized photoreceptive cells. These are modified neurosensory cells. They are negative to normal light intensities,but sudden exposure to a bright light induces burrowing. The entire body appears to be photosensitive, but the proboscis is specially sensitive to light.

REPRODUCTIVE SYSTEM

Asexual reproduction

It is of rare occurence. It is reported by *Gilchrist* (1923) in *Balanoglossus capensis*. During summer the juvenile phase reproduces by cutting off small pieces from the tail end. The separated part later on develops completely into an adult sexual type in next winter.

Sexual reproduction

The sexes are separate but there is no sexual dimorphism. The males are fewer in number than females (1: 60). The gonads are similar in size, shape and position. They are paired, branched or unbranched coelomic sacs found in the branchiogenital region. Each sac is lined with germinal epithelium which is continuous with the ectoderm. By the proliferation of germinal epithelial cells sperms and ova are produced. The ripe sperms and ova are shed in water through a *gonopore*. The ova are larger in size each measures about 1mm in diameter. The sperms are provided with round head. The acrosome is small but distinct. Fertilization is external.

Spawning

The breeding season is from May to June. The suitable temperature needed for this purpose is 16°C. About 2000-3000 eggs are laid embedded

in a mass of mucons escape from the burrow of the female. After about
20 minutes or so the mass of sperms is discharged that leave the male
burrow. Fertilization takes place in sea water. The mucous mass is soon
broken by tidal currents and eggs are dispersed.

Development

In *Balanoglossus*, the eggs are *microlecithal* i.e. contain small amount
of yolk. The development is indirect with a *Tornaria larva*. In *Saccoglossus
kowalevski*, the development is direct without any larval stage.

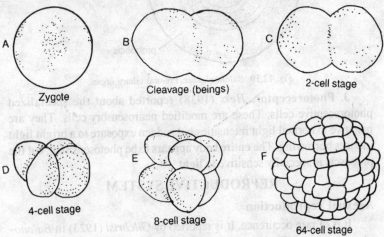

Zygote	Cleavage (beings)	2-cell stage
4-cell stage	8-cell stage	64-cell stage

Fig. 12.20. *Balanoglossus.* Cleavage.

After about six to seven hours of the fertilization the development
starts. The cleavage is *holoblastic*, *equal* and of *radial type*. The first
cleavage is vertical dividing the egg into two equal *blastomeres*. The
second is also vertical but at right angle to the first results in four
blastomeres. The third cleavage furrow is horizontal resulting in eight
blastomeres, the upper four are slightly smaller than lower four and are
called *micromeres*. The lower are *macromeres*. The cleavage continues
for 6-12 hours and results in the formation of hollow *blastula* or
coeloblastula. The coeloblastula is single layered and encloses a central
fluid-filled cavity, the *blastocoel*. Now the blastula flattens along the
animal vegetal axis and invagination takes place on the ventral surface.
The invagination deepens to form the *archenteron*. The archenteron opens
to outside through a pore, the *blastopore*. The blastopore soon closed and
the embryo now called *gastrula*. The gastrula now elongates along the
antero-posterior axis and becomes ciliated. The archenteron divides into
an anterior *protocoel* and a posterior *gut*. The protocoel forms the coelom

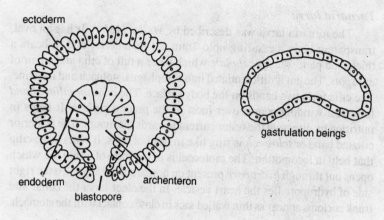

Fig. 12.21. Gastrulation.

of proboscis, thus its origin is *enterocoelic*. The protocoel becomes triangular in shape its one end gets attached to the underside of the apical thickening and another end opens outside through an aperture, the *hydropore*, present on dorsal side. As the protocoel is formed, the inner end of gut moves towards the ventral side and opens out through the *mouth*. The closed blastopore is reopened as *anus*. The gut is differentiated into *oesophagus, stomach* and *intestine*. Now the embryo is known as *Tornaria larva* and it comes out of egg membrane to lead a free swimming life.

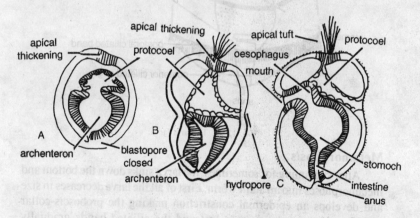

Fig. 12.22. *Balanoglossus*. Development A—gastrula. B—early tornaria. C—young tornaria.

Tornaria larva

The tornaria larva was described by *Muller* (1850). It has an oval, transparent body measuring upto 3mm. At its anterior end, it bears a thickened plate, the *apical plate* which bears a tuft of cilia and a pair of *eye spots*. The gut is differentiated into oesophagus, stomach and intestine. The cilia form two bands on the body surface. The *anterior ciliary band* follows a winding course over most of the preoral surface. It helps in nutrition by directing the water current towards the mouth. The posterior ciliated band or *telotroch* is ring like in front of anus. It bears large cilia that help in locomotion. The protocoel is in the form of a thin sac which opens out through *hydropore* present on dorsal side of larva. To the right side of hydropore lies the heart vesicle. In the older larva the collar and trunk coeloms appear as thin walled sacs in close contact with the stomach.

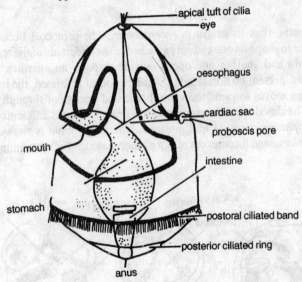

Fig. 12.23. Tornaria larva.

Metamorphosis

After swimming for sometimes. the larva sinks down the bottom and metamorphoses into an adult worm. First of all the larva decreases in size and develops an epidermal constriction making the proboscis-collar boundary. Its transparency is lost and the ciliated bands gradually disappear. The eye spots and apical tuft of cilia are also lost. A second constriction. making the collar-trunk boundary appears. By further

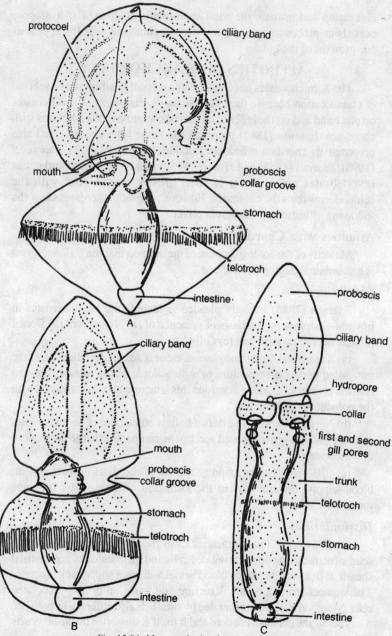

Fig. 12.24. Metamorphosis of tornaria larva.

elongation and growth, the adult condition is attained. The hydropore persists as proboscis pore. Buccal diverticulum and gill-slits appear as out-growths of the gut.

AFFINITIES OF HEMICHORDATA

The hemichordates have most controversial position in the scheme of classification because they possess many characters of invertebrates on one hand and on the other hand they show marked resemblances with chordates. *Bateson* (1885) proposed the name Hemichordata and also proposed its chordata affinities. But *Vander Horst* (1939), *Dawydoff* (1998), *Marcus* (1958) and *Hyman* (1959) ranked the hemichordates as invertebrates on the basis of their greater resemblance with the echinoderms than the chordates. However, the hemichordates show the following affinities with different phyla.

Affinities with Chordates

Majority of the zoologists were of the opinion that the *Balanoglossus* is a chordate though primitive one.

Similarities

Bateson (1885) strongly pleaded to include the hemichordates in phylum-Chordata on the basis of presence of (a) Notochord, (b) Dorsal tubular nervous system and (c) Gill-slits.

(a) *Notochord.* In *Balanoglossus,* there is a short diverticulum of the gut called buccal diverticulum or stomochord, which extends forward into the proboscis. *Bateson* regarded this structure to be homologous with the notochord of chordates.

(b) *Nervous System.* The dorsal hollow collar cord of hemichordates is single and non-ganglionated and can be comparable to the neural cord of vertebrates.

(c) *Gill-slits.* These are similar to those of chordates in development, blood supply, function and in the formation of tongue bars (in some members).

Dissimilarities

(a) *Notochord.* The characteristics of chordate notochord are: it is a solid structure made up of vacuolated cells and surrounded by notochordal sheath. It lies over the dorsal blood vessel and has a supporting function. The stomochord is a hollow structure and made up of non-vacuolated cells. Moreover, it is not surrounded by sheath. It also differs in its position, it lies below the dorsal nerve cord and it itself is supported by the proboscis muscles.

(b) *Nerve cord.* The dorsal tubular nerve cord is confined to the collar region. Elsewhere. it is replaced by solid intra-epidermal nerve strand. Moreover, circumenteric connectives are present. The ventral nerve cord. which is absent in chordates. is present in hemichordates.

The hemichordates further differ from the chordates in:

The absence of paired appendages, metameric segmentation. Absence of exoskeleton, endoskeleton, dermis, liver, red blood corpuscles etc. The division of coelom is peculiar. Body wall is composed of single layered ciliated epithelium; hepatic caeca are present; position of heart vesicle is dorsal. Blood is colourless and numerous gonads are present.

Affinities with Annelida

Spengel (1893) first established affinities between the hemichordates and the annelids. He opposed the view of *Bateson*.

Similarities

1. Both are similar in their morphological features, habits of burrowing and feeding.
2. The proboscis of *Balanoglossus* resembles with the prostomium of annelid worm.
3. Collar of *Balanoglossus* is similar to clitellum of earthworm.
4. In *Balanoglossus* dorsal and ventral blood vessels are present. In annelids, also, both the vessels are present, moreover, the flow of blood is similar in both.
5. Heart is dorsal in both the cases.
6. The alimentary canal is straight and tubular.
7. The Tornaria larva of hemichordates resembles with Trochophore larva of polychaete annelids. In both the larvae apical tuft of cilia, primitive gut, eye spots and ciliary bands are similar. Both the larvae are pelagic.

Dissimilarities

1. Pharyngeal gill-slits are absent in annelids.
2. Stomochord present in *Balanoglossus* is absent in annelids.
3. The nervous system of hemichordates is intra-epidermal. The collar cord is dorsal and hollow. The ventral nerve cord is without ganglia. In annelids a definite nervous system is present that is comprising nerve ring. paired ventral nerve cord and segmental ganglia.
4. In annelids the excretion is performed by nephridia while in hemichordates by glomerulus.
5. Hepatic caeca are absent in annelids.

6. The origin of coelom is schizocoelous in annelids. In hemichordates it is enterocoelous.
7. Cleavage is spiral in annelids but holoblastic in hemichordates.
8. The archenteron is formed by invagination in hemichordates where as in annelids by gradual migration of cells.
9. The Trochophore differs from Tornaria in the presence of nephridia; in the absence of protocoel; blastopore becomes the mouth in Trochophore; in the course of anterior ciliary band.

Affinities with Phoronida

Masterman (1897) advocated relationship of *Balanoglossus* with *Phoronis.*

Similarities

1. Similar nature of epidermal nervous system.
2. Paired gastric diverticula of *Phoronis* like the buccal diverticulum of *Balangolossus.*
3. The *Actinotroch larva* of *Phoronis* has many features of Tornaria larva.
4. Location of lophophore present on mesosome in *Phoronis* as bears the tentaculated arms of *Cephalodiscus* is same.
5. Both have great power of regeneration.
6. Both are tubiculous, vermiform, coelomate bilateria.

Dissimilarities

1. Pharyngeal gill-slits are absent in Phoronida.
2. Excretory organ in *Phoronis* is a pair of metanephridia while glomerulus in hemichordates.
3. The Actinotroch larva possesses larval tentacles.

Affinities with Pogonophora

Marcus (1958) tried to relate Hemichordata with Pogonophora.

Similarities

1. The protocoel remains undivided and contains a pair of coelomoducts and pores to the exterior.
2. Intra-epidermal nervous system.
3. Location of gonads in the trunk.
4. Presence of pericardial sac in some pogonophores.
5. A distinct septum separates the mesocoel from the trunk coelom or metacoel.

Dissimilarities

1. The main nervous mass is located in the protosome.
2. The tentacles originate from the protosome and protocoel extends in all tentacles.
3. The heart and gonopores are dorsal in Hemichordata and ventral in Pogonophora.
4. The Pogonophora lack the gill-slits and alimentation.

Affinities with Echinodermata

Metschinkoff established the affinities of *Balanoglossus* with echinoderms.

An adult hemichordate differs from the adult echinoderm. So that one can hardly suspect any relationship between them. But there are several points of similarities between the larva of *Balanoglossus* i.e. Tornaria larva and the Bipinnaria larva of star-fish. In fact, the Tornaria larva was regarded an echinoderm larva for a long time. Both the larvae show following similarities.

Similarities

1. The larvae are pelagic and transparent.
2. The ciliary band taking up similar course.
3. The nature of alimentary canal is similar.
4. Anus develops at blastoporal end.
5. Early cleavage and gastrulation is same in both.
6. Origin and arrangement of coelom is similar. Proboscis coelom opens out by hydropore in Tornaria is comparable to hydrocoel of Dipleurula larva of echinoderms.

The adults show following resemblances :

1. Coelom is enterocoelous.
2. Heart vesicle and glomerulus of Hemichordata are considered to the dorsal sac and axial gland of echinoderms. Both the structures are closely associated and combine vascular and excretory function.
3. Nervous system is poorly developed.

Dissimilarities

1. The apical plate with eye-spots and apical tuft of cilia are present in Tornaria however, absent in Bipinnaria larva.
2. The telotroch is absent in Bipinnaria larva.
3. Adult echinoderms are radially symmetrical while *Balanoglossus* is bilaterally symmetrical.

Conclusion

On the basis of above similarities between hemichordates and echinoderms, it can be concluded that both the groups have arisen from a common ancestor. There are two views regarding their common ancestry.

Bather's view:

Bather (1900) referred the *Diplurula larva* as a common ancestor. The Diplurula larva is very similar to the mature stages of the Tornaria and the echinoderm larva. However, this view is regarded to be unsatisfactory as it fails to explain ambulacral system of echinoderms.

Grobben's View:

Grobben (1923) regarded the common ancestor as an unattached creature, somewhat, like *Cephalodiscus* with a tentacular apparatus of five arms on each side.

Besides the anatomical and larval resemblances, the serological evidence also carries much importance. The serological studies show that the proteins of hemichordates are related to the echinoderm and chordate proteins. Phosphogens, which are important for muscular tissues also show similarities between hemichordate, echinoderm and chordate.

Barrington (1965) has the opinion based on deuterostome line of chordata evolution. According to him the echinoderms deviated from the acestral stock and formed a bind branch in the main line of evolution. Hemichordates also diverged from the main line of chordate evolution. The main line continued to give rise to the chordates. Thus, hemichordates are placed in a separate invertebrate phylum Hemichordata between Echinodermata and Chordata.

Revision Questions

1. Discuss the affinities and taxonomic position of *Balanoglossus*.
2. Describe the alimentary canal and mode of feeding in *Balanoglossus*.
3. Describe the circulatory system of *Balanoglossus*.
4. Draw neat and well-labelled diagrams of (a) T.S. of *Balanoglossus* through branchiogenital region. (b) T.S. of *Balanoglossus* through proboscis. (c) T.S. of *Balanoglossus* through collar.
5. Write short notes on : (a) Buccal diverticulum. (b) Tornaria larva. (c) Pygochord.

2

Subphylum Urochordata : Characters and Classification

The Urochordates are also known as *Tunicates* (L-*tunica*, an outer covering) or Ascidians (Gr. *askos*, a leather bag). They were classified by *Herdman* on the basis of external morphology and ecological factors. Later on *Lahille* classified them on the basis of pharyngeal modifications. *Garstang* (1895) classified urochordates on the basis of anatomical and embryological features. *Perrier* (1898) divided the urochordates into Enterogona, Pleurogona and Hypogona on the basis of their reproductive organs. The latest classification is given by *Hartmeyer* (1909-1911). There are about 2100 species of urochordates.

Characters

1. Exclusively marine, solitary or colonial, fixed or pelagic, found in all the seas. They are distributed from littoral to abyssal depths.
2. Body varies considerably in size, form and colour. Body is unsegmented and without tail. It is covered by a test or tunic that is why they are also known as *tunicates*.
3. They have two pores related to the atrial and branchial siphons.
4. Coelom is absent. However, an ectodermal lined atrial cavity surrounds the pharynx. The atrial cavity receives gonoducts, anus and gill-slits.
5. In adult the notochord is absent but it is present in larva.
6. Alimentary canal complete with spacious pharynx or branchial sac with endostyle and several pairs of gill-slits.
7. Respiration by gill-slits and test.
8. Circulatory system closed type. Heart is tube like and central in position, which periodically reverses the flow of blood. Special corpuscles, the *vanadocytes* are present which extract vanadium from sea water.
9. Excretion is carried by nephrocytes, neural gland and pyloric glands.

10. In adult the nervous system is represented by a single dorsal ganglion, however, in larva a dorsal tubular nerve cord is present.

11. Usually bisexual, fertilization external. Development indirect through a tadpole larva. Metamorphosis is retrogressive.

12. Asexual reproduction by budding.

CLASSIFICATION

Sub-Phylum Urochordata is divided into three classes

1. Ascidiacea, 2. Thaliacea and 3. Larvacea

Class-1. Ascidiacea

1. These are sessile, solitary or colonial tunicates with dorsal atriopore.

2. Pharynx is perforated, ciliated gill-slits open into the atrial cavity.

3. Sexes are united. Larva is free-swimming and highly developed. It undergoes retrogressive metamorphosis.

4. Adult is without notochord, nerve cord and tail.

5. Asexual reproduction by budding.

Class-Ascidiacea is divided into two orders : Enterogona and Pleurogona.

Order (i) Enterogona

1. Body is sometimes divided into thorax and abdomen.

2. Neural gland is usually ventral to ganglion.

3. Gonad is unpaired and lodged in the intestinal loop or projecting behind it.

4. Larva with two sense organs, the otolith and cerebral eye or ocellus.

Order-Enterogona is divided into two sub-orders : Phlebobranchia and Aplousobranchia.

Sub-order (a) Phlebobranchia

1. Pharynx has an accessory, tubular longitudinal vessel.

2. The intestinal loop is usually along a side of the pharynx.

3. Epicardium in other cases is either sterile or absent.

4. Budding is rare.

Examples : *Ciona, Ascidia, Rhodosoma* etc.

Sub-order (b) Aplousobranchia

1. Pharynx with bars and longitudinal vessels but transverse ridges are present.

2. Body is elongated with distinct abdominal region.

3. The budding is common.

Examples : *Clavelina, Podoclavella.*

Order (ii) Pleurogona

1. Gonads are paired and lie in the atrial wall.
2. Neural gland is dorsal or lateral to the ganglion.
3. Larva has only one sense organ i.e. the otolith. The larval suckers are reinforced by adhesive papillae.
4. Budding is peribranchial and lateral.

   Examples : *Herdmania, Botryllus, Molgula.*

Class-2. Thaliacea

1. These are pelagic and hypopleustonic (animals floating below the surface of water) animals with transparent test.
2. Mouth and atriopore are situated at opposite ends.
3. Body is provided with numerous muscular bands which may encircle the body partially or wholly.
4. Life-cycle shows alternation of generation.
5. These forms reproduce sexually and asexually by complex budding

   This class is divided into three orders : Pyrosomida, Doliolida and Salpida.

Order (i) Pyrosomida

1. Colonial forms hollow floating tubes, which open at one end only.
2. The cavity of the cylinder acts as a common cloaca.
3. Gill-slits are numerous and long.
4. Development is internal, larval stage is lacking.
5. The blastozooids are hermaphrodite and capable of budding. Oozooids are incompletely developed.
6. Each individual has a cerebral eye and a subneural gland with ciliated funnel.
7. They are luminescent.

   Example : *Pyrosoma.*

Order (ii) Doliolida

1. Body is characteristically barrel shaped with thin test. Numerous muscle bands encircling the body.
2. Pharynx is provided with two rows of stigmata, without internal longitudinal bars.
3. The asexual phase is oozooid which reproduces by budding.
4. A tailed larva is present with notochord.

   Examples : *Doliolum, Doliopsis.*

Order (iii) Salpida

1. Body is cylindrical or prism like.
2. The muscular bands are incomplete ventrally and attached to the test dorsally.
3. There is a single pair of very large lateral gill-slit.
4. The development is internal, inside the pouch of the body and the embryo is nourished by a placenta. Larval stage is absent.
5. In the life history alternation of generation is seen (as asexual phase or oozooid and a sexual phase or gonozooid).

   Examples: *Salpa, Thalia, Pegea* etc.

Class-3. Larvacea

1. These are free-swimming, pelagic tunicates.
2. These are neotenic, larval like forms with a persistent notochord.
3. Pharynx possesses only two gill-slits that open directly to outside.
4. Atrium and atriopore are absent.
5. Test or house is a temporary covering with sieve like apertures and performs the function of ciliary feeding.
6. Intestine is normally coiled to the right of the oesophagus.
7. No budding occurs.

   This class is divided into two orders : Endostylophora and Polystylophora.

Order (i) Endostylophora

1. Pharynx is with endostyle.
2. The house is bilaterally symmetrical with separate inhalent apertures.

   Examples : *Appendicularia, Oikopleura, Fritillaria.*

Order (ii) Polystylophora

1. Pharynx without endostyle.
2. House is biradially symmetrical having a single aperture.

   Example : *Kowalevskia*

CIONA

Phylum	-	Chordata
Group	-	Protochordata
Sub-Phylum	-	Urochordata
Class	-	Ascidiacea
Order	-	Enterogona
Genus	-	*Ciona*

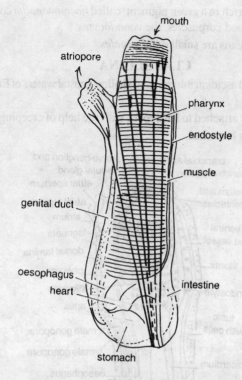

Fig. 2.1. *Ciona*.

1. It is commonly known as 'tube sea-squirt'. It is a solitary and sedentary animal found in shallow sea water attached to the rocks etc.
2. Body is cylindrical, tubular, transparent and longer than broad.
3. Anteriorly it bears eight lobed branchial opening and six lobed atrial opening.
4. Body is covered by a transparent test and through the test longitudinal muscle bands can be seen.
5. Pharynx is perforated but longitudinal internal folds are absent.
6. Intestine has a typhlosole and endostyle.
7. Heart is 'V' shaped.
8. Gonad is single, hermaphrodite and present in the intestinal loop. Ovary is compact and testis branched.
9. Fertilization external. Development indirect through tadpole larva which undergoes retrogressive metamorphosis.

10. The blood is rich in a green pigment, called *haemovanadin* contained in special blood corpuscles, the *vanadocytes*.

11. Excretory organs are small *renal vesicles*.

CLAVELLINA

1. It is a colonial ascidian inhibiting in shallow coastal waters of European seas.

2. Zooids occur attached to hard rocks with the help of creeping stolon.

3. The stolon is branched.

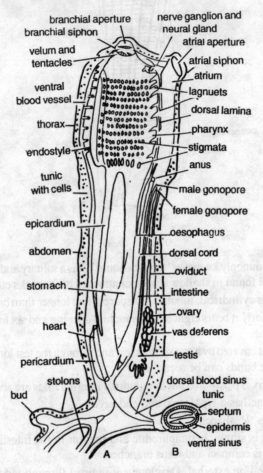

Fig. 2.2. *Clavellina*. A—Single zooid. B—Stolon in T.S.

4. Each zooid is 2.5 cm long and 6 mm broad and remains covered by a transparent test.

5. Body has two distinct regions : upper thorax and lower abdomen. Both are connected by a narrow waiste.

6. In thorax, pharynx with endostyle and dorsal lamina are present. Neural complex, atrium and branchial and atrial siphous are also present.

7. In abdomen heart, alimentary canal, gonad and stolen are present.

8. Gonads are hermaphrodite.

9. *Clavellina* is viviparous as the fertilized eggs develop in atrial cavity.

10. Tadpole larvae are produced and undergo retrogressive metamorphosis forming a young oozoid.

11. Asexual reproduction by budding from stolen forming blastozooids.

12. *Calavellina* forms a connecting link between simple and compound ascidians.

BOTRYLLUS

Phylum	-	Chordata
Group	-	Protochordata
Sub-Phylum	-	Urochordata
Class	-	Ascidiacea
Order	-	Pleurogona
Genus	-	*Botryllus*

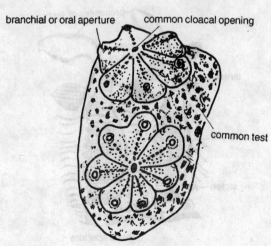

Fig. 2.3. *Botryllus.*

1. It is a sessile, colonial ascidian, widely distributed in European waters and East coast of Atlantic.
2. The individuals or zooids of a coloney are embedded in a common gelatinous and slippery test and are arranged in small star-shaped or rosette-shaped groups.
3. Each group consists of 3-12 zooids arranged around a common cloaca, which receives an elongated atrial siphon from each zooid and opens out by a single common atrial aperture.
4. Each zooid bears 16 small and simple branchial tentacles.
5. The branchial sac bears 7-15 rows of rectangular stigmata.
6. Gonads are paired. Left gonad does not lie in intestinal loop. Hermaphrodite. Fertilization occurs within special cup-like extension of atrial wall. Development indirect through tadpole larva.
7. Asexual reproduction by budding.

PYROSOMA

Phylum	-	Chordata
Group	-	Protochordata
Sub-Phylum	-	Urochordata
Class	-	Thaliacea
Order	-	Pyrosomida
Genus	-	*Pyrosoma*

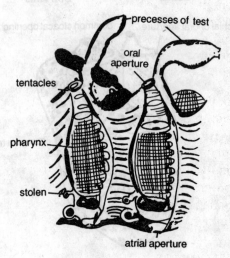

Fig. 2.4. *Pyrosoma.*

1. It is commonly known as 'fire flames'. It is a free swimming colonial form found in warm tropical oceans.
2. The coloney is like a hollow cylinder measuring 25 cm to 1 meter in length.
3. The coloney consists of several zooids called blastozooids embedded in a common test.
4. Blastozooids are arranged in the wall of the cylinder.
5. Branchial and atrial apertures at opposite ends.
6. Test of each zooid is produced into a tongue-like process near mouth and is known as buccal appendage.
7. Branchial sac contains 50 gill-slits divided by internal longitudinal bars.
8. Endostyle and dorsal lamina are present.
9. A large multilobed testis and a small ovary with a single ovum lie behind the gut on ventral side. They are protandrous. Fertilization is endogenous. Cleavage is meroblastic development direct without larval stage.
10. Asexual reproduction by budding.
11. They emit strong light among marine organisms.
12. The Bioluminescent cells are present in endostyle and peripharyngeal bands.

HERDMANIA

The name *Herdmania* was given by *Lahille* (1888). It is a simple ascidian and commonly known as '*sea squirt*' or '*sea-potato*'. There are about 12 species of *Herdmania* but only four of these occur in the Indian ocean. These are *H.pallida, H. ceylonica, H. mauritiana* and *H. ennurensis*. Besides Indian oceans, *H. pallida* is also distributed in the Pacific, Atlantic and Carribean Oceans.

SYSTEMATIC POSITION

Phylum	-	Chordata
Sub-phylum	-	Urochordata
Class	-	Ascidiacea
Order	-	Pleurogona
Genus	-	*Herdmania*

Habits and habitat

It is a marine animal and generally found at places where abundant polychaete fauna (*Turbinella pyrum* and *T.rapa*) and chanks (*Xancus*) are present. Usually they occur in coastal and deeper waters. They remain attached to the rocky substratum by a broad base or embedded in a sandy floor by its extended foot. Sometimes it shows commensal on the shell of *Xancus*. The mollusc carries *Herdmania* from one place to another where it can get more food, oxygen, and dispersal of progenies also occur. The mollusc is protected from its enemies due to presence of unpalatable *Herdmania*. It is a ciliary feeder and feeds on planktons, microorganisms etc. When disturbed, the body contracts and emits two jets of sea-water with a considerable force through the branchial and atrial apertures. Thus the name 'sea-squirt' is given. It is bisexual, however, fertilization is external. The development is indirect with a free swimming tadpole larva which undergoes retrogressive metamorphosis.

EXTERNAL MORPHOLOGY

Shape and size

The animal is roughly oblong or may be slightly elongated because of massive foot. It is laterally compressed. Its size varies between 8-13 cm in length and 6-8 cm in breadth, its thickness is about 4 cm.

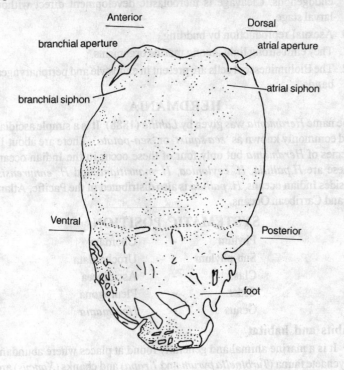

Fig. 2.5. *Herdmania.*

Colour

It is pink in colour in living condition but in preserved condition its colour may be yellowish, greyish or brownish white.

Structure

The body of the animal is encased within a thick protective *test* or *tunic*. Body is divided into a broad *trunk* and a *foot*. The foot is concave ventrally and attached to the substratum. Numerous foreign particles like stones, shell of molluscs, appendages of crustaceans, barnacles etc. are embedded in the foot. At the free upper margin of test there are two protrubrances called *branchial* and *atrial siphons* each bearing a large opening the *branchial aperture* and *atrial aperture* respectively. The branchial aperture is larger measuring 2 cm in diameter while the atrial aperture is smaller measuring 1.5 cm in diameter. Each aperture is boradered by four small lobe-like projections of test called *lips*. The body is covered by a protective test which is usually opaque measuring 2-3 mm in thickness.

Orientation

The branchial aperture marks the anterior end of the animal and the lower end, diagonally opposite to it, is the posterior end. The atrial siphon marks the dorsal side of the animal and opposite to it is ventral side.

Tunic or test

Body is covered by a thick, soft, leathery and translucent covering known as the *test*. The test is secreted by the ectoderm of mantle. It is wrinkled in appearance with a number of folds and depressions running all over the surface. The inner surface is smooth and shining. It wears off continuously from the outer surface and replaced from inside by the epidermis of mantle. The entire foot is made up of test only.

The test is composed of following components :

1. Matrix

The gelatinous matrix is made up of a polysaccharide called *tunicin*, a substance similar to cellulose of plants, but also having proteins and some inorganic substances.

2. Corpuscles

The test cells are six or seven different types according to their specific structures and staining abilities. All the cells are mesodermal in origin.

(a) *Large eosinophilous cells.* These are large ovoidal and nucleated cells with homo-genous cytoplasm. The nucleus is surrounded by a large vesicle.

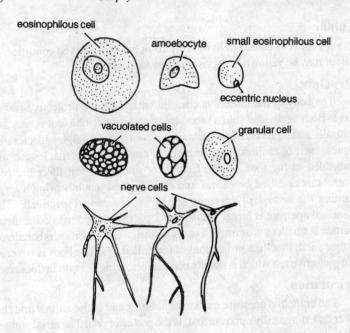

Fig. 2.6. *Herdmania*. Various types of cells found in test.

(b) *Small eosinophilous cells.* These are ovoidal smaller cells. The nucleus is eccentric and the vesicle is absent. Their number is very high.

(c) *Amoeboid cells.* These are amoeba-like cells with changing shape. The nucleus is large. They are fewer in number and scattered widely.

(d) *Vacuolated cells.* These are ovoidal and contain 3-8 vacuoles. The nucleus is usually absent.

(e) *Granular cells.* These cells are concentrated around the nerve cells and fibres. These are slightly bigger than small eosinophilous cells. Each cell contains a large nucleus and granular cytoplasm.

(f) *Small nerve cells.* The cell-body or cyton of the nerve cell may be triangular or irregular. It gives rise two processes which anastomose with each other. The nucleus is large.

(g) *Squamous epithelial cells.* These are flat, polygonal cells containing red pigment from the outer wall of the vascular ampullae.

3. Interlocking fibres

Fine fibrils run criss-cross all through the matrix. Some of them resemble smooth muscle fibres and some nerve fibres.

4. Blood vessels

From the connective tissue of mantle, the blood vessels enter the test. They form anasto-mosing system throughout the test. At the surface of test the branches end into *vascular ampullae* or *terminal knobs.* These ampullae are responsible for red-patches visible on the surface of test. The ampullae are supplied with nerve fibres and perform two functions (i) exchange of gases and (ii) reception of sensation.

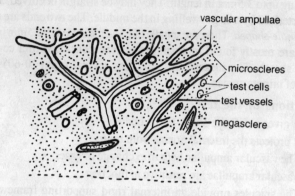

Fig. 2.7. *Herdmania.* V.S. test.

5. Spicules

Besides cells and fibrils, numerous minute calcareous spicules are also found embedded in the matrix of test. These are of two types :

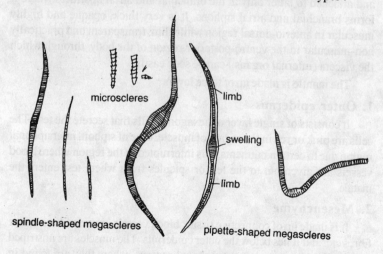

Fig. 2.8. *Herdmania.* Spicules.

(i) *Microscleres.* These are scattered throughout the matrix. Each microsclere consists of a swollen, knob-like head and an elongated tapering body. The body bears several annular rings of minute bristles or spines that are directed towards the head. The size ranges between 50-80μ.

(ii) *Megascleres.* They are quite bigger in size and can be visible with naked eyes. These are not restricted to the test but are found in all parts of the body except the heart. They are of two types-(a) *Pipette shaped*, reaching upto 3.5mm in length. They may be straight or curved. They are characterized by a large swelling in the middle. The two ends are pointed. (b) *Spindle-shaped.* These are spindle like and measure 1.5-2.5mm in length. They are mostly found in small groups each enclosed in a connective tissue sheath. The megascleres also bear several (upto 20-60) annular rings of minute spines.

Functions of the test

1. It gives a definite shape to the body.
2. It protects the internal organs from injury.
3. The vascular ampullae help in exchange of gases.
4. Vascular ampullae are sensitive in function.
5. The spicules provide an internal rigid supporting framework like endoskeleton and keeps the mantle fixed to the test.

BODYWALL OR MANTLE

The bodywall in *Herdmania* is known as *mantle*. It secretes the test and attached to latter only at the branchial and atrial apertures where it forms branchial and atrial siphons. It is very thick, opaque and highly muscular in anterio-dorsal region while thin, transparent and practically non-muscular in the ventro-posterior region of the body, through which the viscera (internal organs) can be seen easily.

The mantle is made up of three layers :

1. Outer epidermis

It consists of single layer of hexagonal cells that secrete the test. The cells are pink or red in the region of muscle, base of siphon, intersiphonal region due to certain pigments. It is interrupted in the region where blood vessels are given out to the test or spicules from where test enters the mantle.

2. Mesenchyme

It is made up of connective tissue, blood vessels, muscle fibres, nerve fibres etc. and it lies below the outer epidermis. The muscles are unstriped and are best developed in the siphonal regions, where they are found in

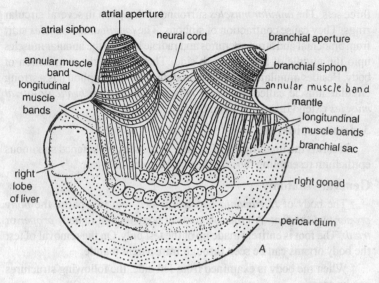

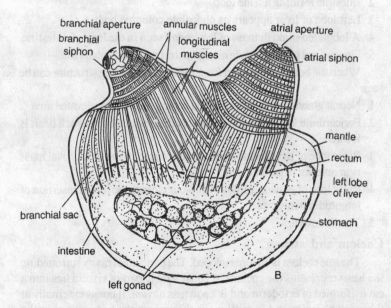

Fig. 2.9. *Herdmania*. (A) Viscera seen from right side (B) Viscera seen from left side.

three sets. The *annular muscles* surround each siphon in several circular rings. They cause contraction of siphons. The *longitudinal muscles* start from branchial and atrial apertures and radiate beneath the annular muscles upto the middle of body on each side. They help in the contraction of body. Besides annular and longitudinal muscles each siphon has a strong circular muscle called *sphincter muscles* and certain *branchio-atrial muscles* extend deeper between the two siphons.

3. Inner epidermis

It forms the inner lining of mantle. It consists of flattened squamous epithelium resembling those of the outer ectodermal layer.

General Anatomy

The body of *Herdmania* can he divided into two parts, the *body proper* and the *foot*. All the soft parts of body remain in body *proper* or *trunk*. The foot is entirely made up of the test only. On the removal of test the body organs can be seen through transparent mantle.

When the body is examined from left side, the following structures can be seen:

1. Two projecting siphons with their annular and longitudinal muscles.
2. Intestine forming a wide loop.
3. Left lobe of liver appears as chocolate coloured body.
4. A lobulated pinkish mass of left gonad seen in the loop of intestine.
5. Opaque rod like endostyle along ventral margin of pharynx.

When the body is examined from right side following structure can be seen :

1. Neural gland in the inter-siphonal region forming an elevated area.
2. Pericardium looks like a transparent crescentric tube in which heart is located.
3. Right lobe of liver forms a chocolate coloured more or less oval mass near anterior of pericardium.
4. Right lobe of gonads, pinkish in colour close to the line of insertion of longitudinal muscles.
5. The endostyle.

Coelom and atrium

The true coelom is underdeveloped. The pericardial cavity surrounding the heart represents the coelom. A considerable part of viscera lies into a cavity formed of ectoderm and is known as *atrium*. It opens externally at the atrial aperture and is continuous throughout the body except in the anterior and mid-ventral part. where branchial sac is fused with body wall.

Its median dorsal part is known as *cloaca* where rectum and genital ducts empty their contents. The remaining part surrounding the branchial sac or pharynx from the sides is called the *peribranchial cavity*.

DIGESTIVE SYSTEM

The digestive system includes the alimentary canal and digestive glands.

1. Alimentary canal

The alimentary canal is complete and coiled. It is divisible into four zones :

I. Ingressive zone- comprising mouth and buccal cavity.

II. Progressive zone - includes pharynx, oesophagus and   stomach

III. Degressive zone - includes intestine.

IV. Egressive zone - comprises the rectum.

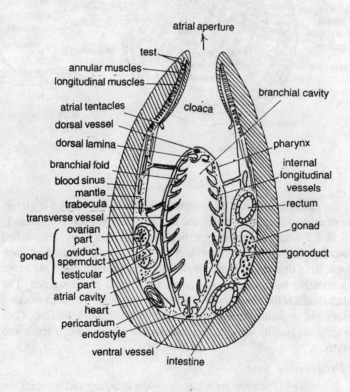

Fig. 2.10. *Herdmania*. Section of the body.

I. Ingressive zone

1. *Mouth*. The mouth or branchial aperture lies on the top of branchial siphon. It is bordered by four lips formed by the test. These lips are contractile in nature. Mouth leads into buccal cavity.

2. *Buccal cavity*. The buccal cavity lies in the branchial siphon. It is lined with the ectoderm and test. At the base of buccal cavity lies a strong *branchial sphincter*. Just above the sphincter lies the circlet of highly branched *branchial tentacles*.

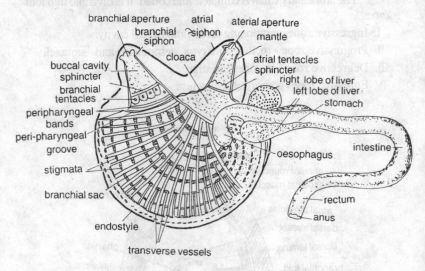

Fig. 2.11. *Herdmania*. Alimentary canal.

The tentacles are about 64 in number and are of four sizes, 8 are large, 8 are medium, 16 are small and 32 are smallest. Each tentacle is bipinnately branched, bearing several symmetrically paired lateral branches called tentaculets. Each tentaculet bears secondary and tertiary branches. Each tentacle has a thin covering of a single layered epithelium enclosing a core of connective tissue containing nerve fibrils and blood sinuses. The epithelial cells of the lower, concave border are glandular. Tentacles working as sieve and straining the water current passing into branchial sac. They also taste the quality of water thus act as *chaemoreceptor*. It leads into pharynx.

II. Progressive zone

3. *Pharynx*. The pharynx is large sac-like structure and occupies the major part of atrial cavity. It is differentiated into two very unequal zones :

(a) Prebranchial zone and (b) Branchial sac.

(a) *Prebranchial zone*. It is a small anterior region just behind the branchial sphincter. It is demarcated from the branchial sac by two circular, parallel ciliated ridges called *anterior* and *posterior peripharyngeal bands*. Between the bands there is a narrow ciliated groove called *peripharyngeal groove*. The anterior peripharyngeal band is a complete ring while the posterior peripharyngeal band is incomplete, dorsally it is continuous with *dorsal lamina* or *hyperpharyngeal groove* of branchial sac and ventrally with *endostyle*. Just above the anterior peripharyngeal band on dorsal side there lies a swollen horse-shoe shaped structure, the *dorsal tubercle*.

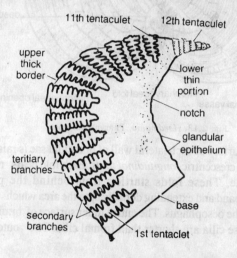

Fig. 2.12. *Herdmania*. Branchial tentacle (side view).

(b) *Branchial sac*. It is a large specious structure. Its lateral walls are perforated by numerous elongated *gill-slits* or *stigmata*. There are about 200,000 stigmata on each side of branchial sac. The stigmata establish a communication between pharynx and the atrial cavity. The stigmata are arranged in several transverse rows. The epithelial lining of the stigmata bears long cilia, called *lateral cilia*. They almost cover the stigmata, so that food particles do not escape through them. Between the stigmata are *external transverse* and *internal longitudinal vessels* through which blood flows. These vessels divide the pharyngeal wall into squarish or rectangular stigmatic areas. Each area has 5-6 stigmata. Besides the transverse and longitudinal vessels, there are *interstigmatic transverse* and *longitudinal vessels*. These are fine vessels.

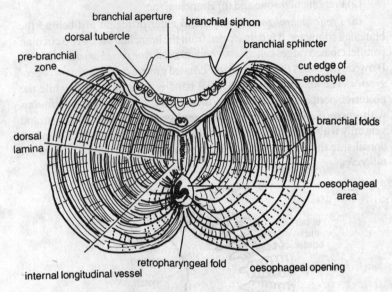

Fig. 2.13. *Herdmania*. Pharynx cut open.

The inner surface of each lateral wall of branchial sac is raised into 9 or 10 prominent crescentric *longitudinal folds.* Each fold bears numerous hollow papillae. These folds starting from behind the posterior peripharyngeal band and extending dorsally upto the area which surround the opening of the oesophagus. The entire inner surface of branchial sac bears cilia. These cilia are shorter than frontal cilia. The outer wall of

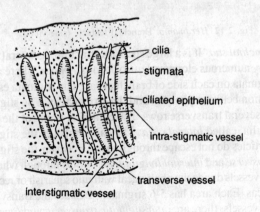

Fig. 2.14. Stigmata and blood vessels of branchial wall.

branchial sac is connected to the mantle by several hollow strands, called *trabeculae*, each containing a blood vessel.

On the ventral side, there is a mid-ventral longitudinal groove, the *endostyle* or *hypobranchial groove*. It starts from the ventral margin of the posterior peripharyneal band running ventrally and terminating into a pit, short distance from the oesophageal opening on the dorsal side, but its walls extend upto the oesophageal opening, as the *retro-pharyngeal bands*. The endostyle is lined with five longitudinal tracts of ciliated cells alternating with four longitudinal strips of non-ciliated cells (these tracts are glandular and secrete mucous). The cilia of the median tract are much longer than other cilia.

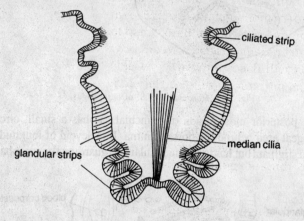

Fig. 2.15. *Herdmania*. T.S. of endostyle.

On the dorsal side, a thin flap called *hyperpharyngeal band* or *dorsal lamina* hangs in the branchial sac. Anteriorly it starts from the posterior

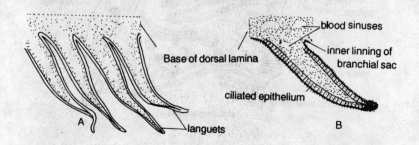

Fig. 2.16. *Herdmania*. Dorsal Lamina A -Side view. B T.S.

peripharyngeal band and extends posteriorly upto the right lip of oesophageal opening. The dorsal lamina bears a row of 20-30 ciliated tongue-like structures called *languets*. In living animal the languets are turn on right side forming a sort of gutter.

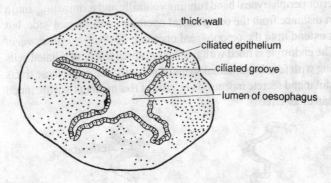

Fig. 2.17. *Herdmania*. T.S. of oesophagus.

The posterior most region of branchial sac has a small, circular oesophageal area behind the dorsal lamina. It is devoid of longitudinal folds and stigmata but has two semicircular lips guarding the oesophageal opening.

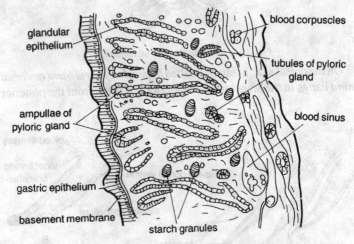

Fig. 2.18. *Herdmania*. T.S. of stomach.

4. *Oesophagus.* The branchial sac posteriorly opens into the oesophagus. It is a short, thick and curved tube without stigmata. It bears four longitudinal ciliated grooves on its inner surface for the passage of food.

5. *Stomach.* It is a wide, thin walled tube with almost smooth inner surface. It bears sphincters at each end. It is surrounded on either side by left and right lobes of liver.

III. Degressive zone

6. *Intestine.* The stomach passes into intestine which is a thin walled 'U' shaped tube consisting of a proximal limb and a distal limb. The proximal limb runs nlong the ventral side, than takes a sharp turn to dorsal side to become the distal limb, leading into the rectum. The left gonad lodges between two limbs.

IV. Egressive zone

7. *Rectum.* It is the small terminal part of alimentary canal that curves dorsally to open in the atrial cavity by the anus. The rectal lining is made up of flagellated epithelium.

2. Digestive glands

The liver and pyloric glands are the digestive glands which are associated with alimentary canal.

1. Liver

The liver of *Herdmania* is a large chocolate coloured bilobed gland. Its left tobe is larger and the right lobe is smaller. Both the lobes lie on either side of stomach. Each lobe is made up of a large number of tubules embedded in a connective tissue matrix and contains blood sinuses. It secretes a dark yellowish-brown secretion which is poured in the stomach by 10 or 11 fine ciliated *hepatic ducts*. Each duct opens independently. The secretion contains *amylase, protease* and a mild *lipase* enzymes.

2. Pyloric gland

It consists of a large number of branching tubules in the wall of stomach and intestine. The tubules of gland open into a duct and a number of ducts unite to form a single duct which opens into the middle of proximal limb of intestine. Most probably this gland performs excretory function as well as pancreas of higher vertebrates.

Food, feeding and digestion

The food of *Herdmania* is planktons (protozoans, fragments of decaying animals, algae etc.). The animal adopt filter-feeding methods. A continuous water current is set by the rapid beating of the cilia of stigmata.

Along this water current food particles enter the branchial sac where they are picked up in the mucous cord by the ciliary action of endostyle. Dorsal lamina and pharyngeal bands also play important role. There are two views regarding feeding mechanism :

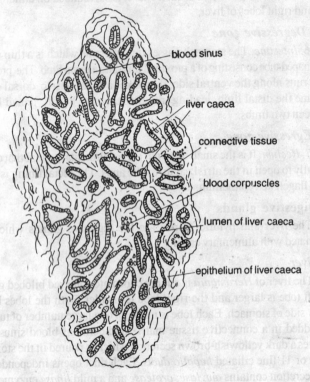

blood sinus

liver caeca

connective tissue

blood corpuscles

lumen of liver caeca

epithelium of liver caeca

Fig. 2.19. *Herdmania*. T.S. of liver lobe.

1. According to *Willey* and *Herdman* a constant flow of water along food particles is maintained through the mouth via the stigmata to atrial aperture. The food particles are checked by the lateral cilia of stigmata. At the same time the mucous is secreted by glandular cells of endostyle. The mucous is carried forward by the ciliary action. Near the pharyngeal bands the mucous cord is divided into two halves and run in between the peripharyngeal bands. In the peripharyngeal region the food particles are caught and entangled in the mucous. The cilia of bands carry this food loaded mucous cord to the dorsal side where one cord is again formed and transfered into the food passage formed by dorsal lamina.

2. *Das, Orton* and *Mac Guinte* objected the above view. According to them the mucous secreted by endostyle spreads transversely along the either sides of endostyle by the lashing movement of the long median and lateral cilia. In this way the mucous is constantly being forced to the dorsal lamina rolled up into a cylindrical mass. Finally the mucous is carried backwards into the oesophageal opening. From oesophagus the food passes into the stomach.

The liver is the main digestive gland in *Herdmania*. The secretion of liver is a mixture of powerful amylase, protease and weak lipase. Bile pigments are also present. Pyloric gland probably has an accessory function in digestion. Complete digestion occurs in the proximal limb of intestine and absorption mainly takes place in the mid-intestinal part. The undigested food material is passed into rectum and is discharged into atrial siphon through anus.

The reserve food material is starch-like granules in the liver.

RESPIRATORY SYSTEM

The special respiratory organs are absent, entire branchial sac and the folds of its inner wall serves as respiratory surface where exchange takes place between the blood and dissolved oxygen in water current coming out through the stigmata. The pharyngeal wall is highly vascular traversed by rich network of blood vessels. Presence of the lacunae in the tissue of branchial sac and hollow papillae facilitate the rapid exchange of the gases. The test also provides a respiratory surface as it contains vascular ampullae and blood vessels.

Blood Vascular System

The circulatory system consists of *heart* and *pericardium, blood vessels* and *blood*.

Heart and pericardium

A contractile heart is situated in the pericardium. The pericardium is about 7cm long and 3 mm wide. It is situated below the right gonad and is visible through the mantle. It is closed at both the ends and its cavity remains filled with a fluid having corpuscles like found in the blood. In the centre of pericardial cavity there is a pear- shaped body which moves with the direction of blood since there is no valve in the heart to regulate it. The pericardium is thick walled and is composed of connective tissue contains blood sinuses and internally lines with squamous epithelium.

The heart is thin walled tubular and contractile structure lies in the pericardial cavity. It remains attached throughout its whole length to the

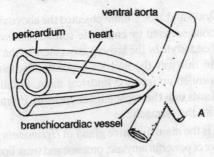

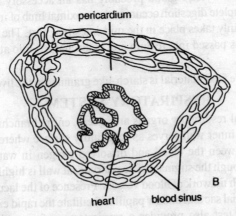

Fig. 2.20. *Herdmania*. (A) Pericardium and enclosed heart (B) T.S. pericardium and heart.

pericardium with the help of a long flap. The heart is internally composed of epithelium and externally by a striated muscular layer.

Blood vessels

There are about four main blood vessels which simultaneously, once serve as the arteries and at other movement these become the veins depending upon the direction of blood flow.

1. Ventral aorta

It is the largest vessel. Just after its emergence from the ventral side of heart. it gives rise three branches: an *anterior limb*, a *posterior limb* and *ventral test vessel*. The anterior limb runs forward and towards the branchial siphon it unites with *peripharyngeal vessel*. Just near their junction a short *subtentacular vessel* is given to siphon. Sub-tentacular vessel sends a *tentacular* branch in each branchial tentacle and about 6 - 8 *siphonal vessels* into the branchial siphon. The posterior limb. at its extremity, gives off a small vessel to the oesophagus. Both anterior and posterior limbs of ventral aorta send numerous paired *transverse branchial vessels* in the branchial sac which run transversely in between the rows of stigmata. Their number ranges between 40-56 paris.

Ventral aorta sends out blood into the test through a large *ventral test vessel* which arises from the junction of ventral aorta and heart.

2. Dorsal aorta

This is a large vessel as thick as the ventral aorta. It runs to the dorsal wall of branchial sac just above the dorsal lamina. Anteriorly it gives out a short *neural vessel* to the neural gland and a small branch to the dorsal tubercle. After that it joins the peripharyngeal, sub-tentacular vessels and

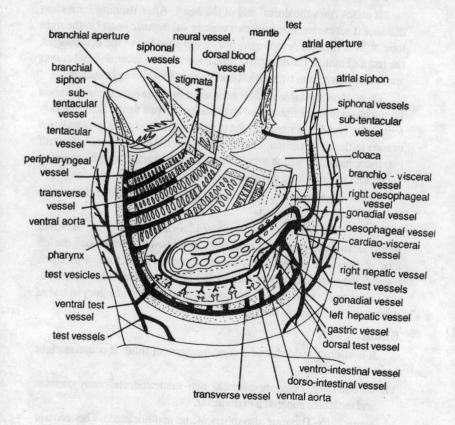

Fig. 2.21. *Herdmania.* Blood-vessels.

6 - 8 siphonal vessels. Posteriorly, it joins the *branchio-visceral vessel*. In the middle region it sends *transverse branchial vessels* that joins similar vessels coming from ventral aorta.

3. Branchio-visceral vessel

The branchial and visceral vessels commonly originate from the posterior end of dorsal aorta. It gives rise two branches: (a) *Right oesophageal vessels* supplies the blood to the right oesophageal lip and right liver lobe. (b) The *ventro-intestinal vessel* which runs along the ventral wall of intestine and supplies to left lip of oesophagus, left lobe of liver, stomach and intestine.

4. Cardio-visceral vessel

It arises from the dorsal end of the heart. After running for a short distance it gives rise following two vessels. (a) *hepatic vessel* to the right lobe of liver and (b) *oesophagio-test vessel* supplies to the oesophagus, the test and mantle (middle part). The main cardio-visceral vessel curves and takes a turn from right to left and gives off following branches :

(i) *Median dorsal branch*. It goes straight to the base of atrial siphon giving blood to atrial siphon and its tentacles where it forms a circular *sub-tentacular vessel* that runs near the base of siphon and gives 6 - 8 *siphonal vessels* in the atrial siphon. Just near the heart the dorsal branch gives off two more branches which supply blood to right gonad as *right gonadial vessel* and to the left lip of oesophageal as *left oesophageal vessel*.

(ii) *Left gonadial branch*. It is the main middle branch that passes obliquely into the left gonad.

(iii) *Ventral branch of cardio-visceral*. Soon after its origin, the vessel gives rise two branches: (a) *Jorso-intestinal branch*. It runs along the left lobe of liver and stomach and supply blood to them then it proceeds towards the intestinal region and supplies blood to dorsal side of intestine. (b) The second vessel again ramified into two vessels one goes in test as *dorsal test* and other to the stomach.

Blood

It is slightly reddish and almost transparent fluid. It contains eight types of corpuscles:

1. *Orange cells*. These are spherical, non-nucleated, uniformly granular and measures about 11μ in diameter.
2. *Signet cells*. These are also spherical and non-nucleated. They contain a large vacuole. Their average size is $10\ \mu$.

3. *Green cells*. These are also known as *vanadocytes*. They are spherical, non-nucleated, yellowish green and contain about 5-6 vacuoles. The cytoplasm is finely granular. They extract vanadium from sea-water.

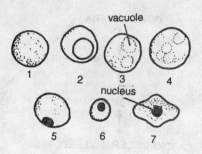

Fig. 2.22. *Herdmania*. Blood corpuscles.

4. *Compartment cells*. These are non-nucleated, light yellow cells. Numerous vacuoles are present in cytoplasm.

5. *Eosinophilous cells*. They possess an eccentric nucleus. The cytoplasm contains brown granules.

6. *Lymphocytes*. These are oblong and smallest in size. They posses a large centrally placed nucleus and measure about 4-5μ.

7. *Macrophages*. These are coursely granular amoeboidal cells having blunt pseudopodia.

8. *Nephrocytes*. These are vacuolated cells containing colloidal suspensions.

Course of Circulation

The circulation of blood through the heart and vessels is peculiar type, once oxygenated blood passes through the heart and vessels, the next movement deoxygenated blood takes its turn through the same vessels. Thus the heart acts as a '*systemic pump*' and a '*branchial pump*', alternately for short periods.

This change in the direction of blood circulation is initiated by heart which once beats from dorsal to ventral side for about 2-3 minutes. suddenly stops beating for a few seconds, and resumes beating in reverse direction. Again the beating is stopped and resumed in dorso-ventral direction. It is controlled by the pear-shaped body present in pericardial cavity.

NEURAL COMPLEX

The nervous system, excretory system and associated receptor organs are together called *neural complex*.

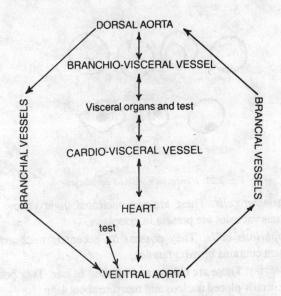

Fig. 2.23. *Herdmania.* Course of blood circulation.

Nervous system

The nervous system is represented by a solid, elongated dorsal ganglion. It lies between the branchial and atrial siphons forming the central nervous system. It is pinkish in colour and almost equal to the neural gland. The peripheral nervous system is represented by five slender

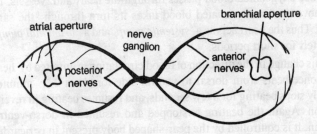

Fig. 2.24. *Herdmania.* Nervous system.

nerves, three arising from the anterior and two from the posterior end of the ganglion. The anterior nervous supply to the branchial tentacles, branchial siphons and muscles. The posterior nerves encircle the base of atrial siphon and supply nerves to the muscles, epithelium of atrial siphon, test, gut and other viscera.

The sense organs

The receptors are poorly developed in *Herdmania*. Following are the sensory structures:

1. *Tangoreceptors*. These are modified cells which are present in the nonvascular epidermal layer of test. They cover the ampullae, tentacles and marginal cells of both the siphons.

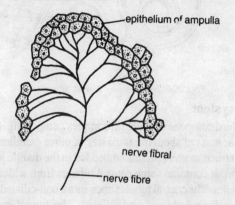

Fig. 2.25. *Herdmania*. Nerve supply to vascular ampullae.

2. *Pigmented photoreceptors*. These are bright red pigmented spots present in the siphonal lining and are considered to be sensitive to light.

3. *Olfactoreceptors*. The tentacles are richly supplied with nerve fibres, which are capable to taste the quality of water and size of food particles.

4. *Rheoreceptors*. According to *Das* these are present on the apical margin of the siphons.

5. *Thermoreceptors*. Cell-lining the siphons are very sensitive to changes in the temperature of water.

6. *Dorsal tubercle*. It is the second component of neural complex. It is situated mid-dorsally in peribranchial region. It has a broad base and two spirally coiled cones arise from the base. In each cone a spirally coiled ciliated channel makes three coils. Channels of two sides meet at the base. There is a funnel shaped shallow ciliated opening of neural gland in the

centre. It is an olfactorious gustato-receptor as it tastes the quality and smell of water.

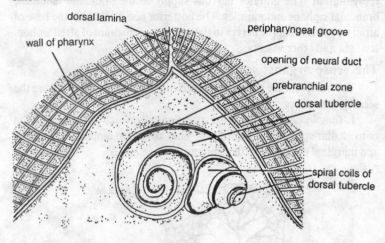

dorsal lamina

wall of pharynx

peripharyngeal groove

opening of neural duct

prebranchial zone

dorsal tubercle

spiral coils of dorsal tubercle

Fig. 2.26. *Herdmania*. Dorsal tubercle.

Excretory system

It is the third component of neural complex comprising *neural gland*. It is a glandular mass of about the same size of nerve ganglion. It is brown and elliptical structure and remains embedded in the mantle just above the nerve ganglion. It contains some central tubules from which arise a few peripheral tubules. The central tubules open into a non-ciliated canal whose anterior part is funnel shaped and ciliated. The funnel opens into the dorsal part of branchial sac at the base of dorsal tubercle. The excretory

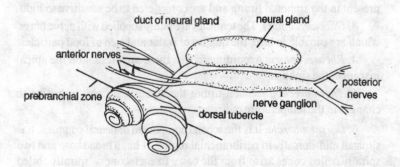

duct of neural gland

neural gland

anterior nerves

posterior nerves

prebranchial zone

nerve ganglion

dorsal tubercle

Fig. 2.27. *Herdmania*. Neural complex.

cells infact are *nephrocytes* of the blood. These cells are brown in colour and contain xanthine and urate as excretory products. When these cells are filled with excretory granules they pass into the lumen of nerual gland.

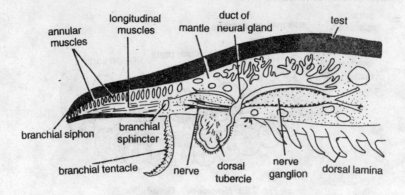

Fig. 2.28. *Herdmania*. Section of neural complex.

Recently *Das* (1956) has shown that besides excretory function the neural gland secretes a hormone. It is believed that this hormone stimulates the egg-laying and also accelerates the rate of development and metamorphosis. This hormone is similar to gonadotropin of higher vertebrate secreted by pituitary. This confirms the view of *Julin* (1881) that the neural gland of *Herdmania* is morphologically equivalent of the pituitary body of vertebrates. This view is confirmed by the findings of *Bacq* and *Florkin*.

REPRODUCTIVE SYSTEM

Herdmania is hermaphrodite,but self-fertilization is not possible because of different periods for gonads maturation.The animal is *protogynous*.

Gonads

A pair of gonad gradually tapering towards the atrial side. The left gonad lies in intestinal loop while the right gonad lies above the pericardium. The gonads are embedded in mantle. Each gonad consists of 10-25 lobes arranged in two rows. The median lobe is bigger in size and is bean shaped while the other lobes are rounded or oval. Each lobe is bisexual and consisting of a large peripheral *testicular zone* of a brick-red colour and an inner smaller *ovarian zone* of a light-red or pink colour. The testicular zone is made up of closely packed *spermatic caeca* lined by germinal epithelium forming *spermatogonia*. The spermatogonia give rise to spermatozoa by spermatogenesis. The ovarian zone consists of follicular wall from which fully formed ova drop into the follicular cavity. Some of germinal cells budded off from the follicular wall but they fail to develop into ova and differentiated as follicular cells.

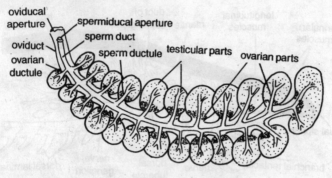

Fig. 2.29. *Herdmania*. Gonad.

Gonoduct

Each gonad has two gonoducts, *oviduct* and *spermatic duct* or vas deferens runing along the central axis. The oviduct is considerably wider than vas deferens and running along the outer or atrial side, opens at its dorsal end into the atrial cavity by a four lipped *oviducal aperture* situated a short distance behind the anal aperture.

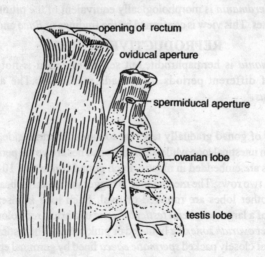

Fig. 2.30. *Herdmania*. Showing opening of rectum, oviduct and spermatic duct.

The vas deferens is formed by the union of *spermatic ductules,* one from testicular zone of each lobe. Vas deferens runs along the branchial or inner side of the oviduct and opens independently into cloaca by *spermiducal aperture.* Both, oviduct and vas deferens, are internally lined by cilia.

Gametes

The male gametes are *spermatozoa* or *sperms.* A mature spermatozoon measures about 4µ in length and as usual has an anterior broad *head, a middle piece* and a long *tail.* The head is capped with *acrosome.* The *ovum* is large and contains small amount of yolk *(microlecithal).* The nucleus is large and eccentric. It is surrounded by a thin *vitelline membrane* and a tough inner *chorion.* Between the two membranes is the *perivitelline fluid* containing a few scattered follicular cells of the ovary that secrete the chorion. Some follicular cells are arranged to form an *inner follicular layer* round the vitelline membrane. Follicular cells of the ovary finally secrete the *outer chorion.* The *inner chorionic fluid* separates the outer and inner chorionic membranes.

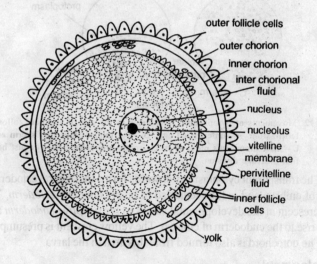

Fig. 2.31. *Herdmania.* An ovum.

EMBRYOLOGY OF *HERDMANIA*

Fertilization

The fertilization is external and takes place in sea-water. Since *Herdmania* is protogynous, self-fertilization is avoided. Mature spermatozoa and ova are liberated into the cloaca from where they pass into the sea. The enterance of spermatozoon into the egg is marked by certain movements of ooplasm. After fertilization, three separate zones are clearly demakated. These are : (a) a clear cytoplasm, (b) a yellow crescent of lipoidal inclusions and (c) the gray yolky region. A fourth light gray crescent, anterio-dorsally is also visible.

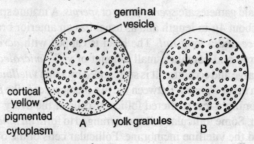

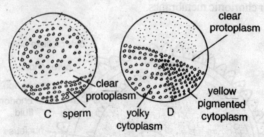

Fig. 2.32. Movements of cytoplasmic substances in the egg of ascidian, following fertilization. A—unfertilized egg; B—egg immediately after sperm entry; C—male pronucleus move to meet female pronucleus; D—egg just before first cleavage division.

The transparent cytoplasm after wards forms the general ectodermal layer of embryo and is thus regarded to be *presumptive ectoderm*. The gray crescent at the developmental stages in *presumptive endoderm* as it gives rise to the endoderm of embryo. The yellow crescent is presumptive tail. The notochord is also formed from this area in the larva.

Development

The development of *Herdmania* has been described by *S.M. Das* and *Sebastain*.

Cleavage

The cleavage is *holoblastic* and approximately *equal*. After half an hour of fertilization, the first cleavage takes place. It is meridional as it passes through the polar axis and bisects the zygote into two blastomeres. The second division is also meridional and occurs at the right angle of first cleavage. The third cleavage is horizontal as a result 8 cells are formed arranged in two ties. By further divisions a flattened blastula is formed having a small segmentation cavity called *blastocoel*. Blastula contains 64-128 blastomeres. It takes about 110 minutes.

Gastrulation

Gastrulation starts after 6th cleavage by *emboly* and followed by in sinking of macromeres resulting the formation of archenteron which completely obliterates the blastocoel. The opening of archenteron is blastopore. It forms the posterior end of gastrula and gradually closes by the growth of its margin. The gastrulation is completed within 110 minutes.

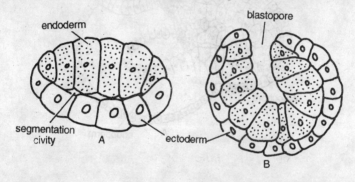

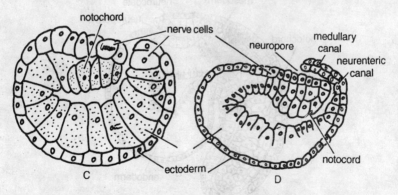

Fig. 2.33. Early development of ascidian. A—Flattened blastula; B—Early gastrula; C—Advanced gastrula; D—Later gastrula.

A fully formed gastrula is bilayered embryo with a large archenteron and no traces of blastocoel. Its outer layer consists of the presumptive ectoderm all over except a band of presumptive neural plate on the dorsal side. The inner layer is made up of presumptive endoderm with a presumptive notochord in mid-dorsal region and presumptive mesodermal strips in dorso-lateral parts.

Organogenesis

Immediately after the completion of gastrulation, the organogenesis is set in. The embryo elongates in the direction of future long axis. The dorsal surface become recognizable by being flatter, while the ventral surface remains convex and forms the primary organ rudiments.

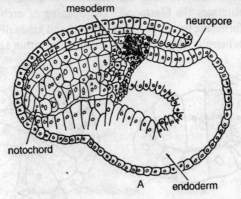

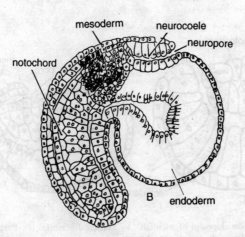

Fig. 2.34. A—Median optical section of larva with medullary canal communicating to the exterior by neuropore and with the archenteron by neurenteric canal; B—larva with rudiments of the tail, mesoderm and notochord.

1. Neurogenesis

The presumptive neural plate occupying the mid-dorsal line sinks inwards and rolls up its margins to form the *medullary groove*. The folds of groove unite to form the *neural tube*. The neural tube extends into the tail. Its anterior part enlarges to form a *cerebral vesicle*. In the cerebral vesicle *ocelli* and *statolith* are formed. At the anterior end, the neural canal remains open to the exterior for some times by an opening called, the *neuropore*. The embryo at this stage of development is called *neurala*.

2. Notogenesis

The notochord is formed from presumptive notochord lying in the roof of the archenteron. They arrange to form an elongated cord of cells which become completely constricted off from the endoderm of the wall of archenteron and come to lie between medullary groove and archenteron.

3. Mesogenesis

The presumptive mesoderm strips separate from the archenteron and give rise to a pair of longitudinal strands of cells forming the mesodermal rudiments. Now the archenteron is entirely formed by endoderm.

FORMATION OF LARVA

The embryo becomes pear-shaped and its posterior end forms the tail rudiment. At the anterior region, the trunk now becomes oval. At its anterior end appear three processes of the ectoderm called the rudiments of the adhesive papillae.

Structure of larva

Larva is developed from embryo about 10-20 hrs after the egg is fertilized. Hatching occurs in water so the larva which is *tadpole* leads free swimming life. Tadpole larva is small, elongated and some what cylindrical in out line and measures about 1.2 to 1.5mm (trunk 0.30 mm and the tail 0.85mm) in length and 0.2 to 0.3 mm in width. The entire body of the tadpole can be divided into two parts : the *trunk* and the *tail*. The trunk is short and measures about 0.3mm. The trunk is surrounded by a thin and transparent covering the *test*, which becomes flattened in the tail region and forms a *tail fin*. The tail which is vibratile in nature is about four times as long as the trunk, and is also laterally compressed.

At the anterior end of the larva, there are three adhesive papillae which are provided with ectodermal secretory cells whose secretion helps in the attachment of the larva with the substratum during metamorphosis. Of the three papillae, two are dorso-lateral in position while third one is ventro-median in position. Larval sense organs which are in the form of

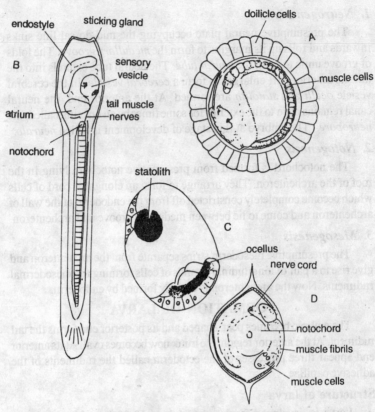

Fig. 2.35. Development. (a) Tadpole ready to hatch, (b) Tadpole, (c) T.S. of Tail.

paired *ocelli* or eyes and single unpaired *otolith,* are situated towards the dorsal side of the trunk. Otolith and ocelli are lodged in *sensory* or *cerebral vesicle* which is hollow and oval in outline. The wall of the sensory vesicle is made up of single cell in thickness. Both the ocelli not only differ from each other in size but also in location. One ocellus which is oval in shape is larger and is situated postero-dorsally while other ocellus is rounded in shape and is smaller in size. This ocellus is antero-ventral in position. The otolith is the balancing organ in larva and is situated obliquely from the ventral wall of the sensory vesicle. The otolith is a unicellular structure having a spherical, dark pigmented body at its end. Behind the sensory vesicle. *visceral ganglion* is situated which is more or less solid ganglion. The visceral ganglion is made up of large cells with round nuclei. The visceral ganglion is continued posteriorly in the form of a hollow nerve cord which is situated above the notochord in the mid dorsal region of the tail. In larva it is extended up to the tip of tail. The nerve cord of tadpole can be compared with the spinal cord of the higher chordates.

Ventral to the nerve cord is a cylindrical *notochord* which is made up of a single row of large vacuolated turgid cells. The notochord persists only in the tail region. In the trunk region it extends for a very short distance and is covered over by a notochordal sheath as well as the longitudinal muscle bands. The muscle bands are normally three pairs on the sides of notochord and a single muscle band on its ventral side. Out of lateral three pairs one pair is dorsolateral, the other ventro-lateral and the 3rd is lateral in position. Towards the free end of the tail, the lateral pairs normally disappear.

In tadpole alimentary canal is fully developed. The opening of mouth and atriopore are situated on the dorsal side of the trunk. Mouth remains covered by test, so no feeding is possible. The opening of mouth is formed by an ectodermal invagination and endodermal evagination, both joining to form a common partition which later on disappears. The opening of atriopore slightly differs in development from the mouth. It develops as an invagination of the ectoderm above the nerve cord. The invagination sends out diverticulae to the sides of the nerve cord, notochord and finally they extend over the lateral phase of the pharynx. After covering the pharynx the atrial diverticulae join with the wall of the pharynx and the first gill-slit appears on the left side. This gill-slit is a perforation between ectodermal layer of atrium and the endodermal layer of the wall of pharynx. After the first gill-slit the succeeding gill-slits are added posteriorly. The alimentary canal behind the pharynx is differentiated as a short tube forming the oesophagus, rounded stomach and a long tubular intestine. The intestine requires an opening dorsally into the atrium.

From the cavity of pharynx a diverticulum towards the ventral side, is given out which gives rise to the formation of pericardium. The pericardium for sometime retains its connection with gut and later on separates out as an individual sac. The pericardium then inside its body develops other tube by the process of invagination from its dorsal wall. This tube is the heart which retains its connection with the pericardium by a dorsal mesentery.

Retrogressive Metamorphosis

In *Herdmania* and other ascidians tadpole larva develops during ontogeny, where it leads free swimming life for three to four hours. Here in this case as the life of tadpole is very short and the mouth is closed so no feeding activity is performed by the larva. The larva is *geonegative* and *photopositive* that is why it swims on water surface in bright light. But during metamorphosis the larva becomes *photonegative* and *geopositive*. i.e. larva moves away from light and settles down to the bottom and becomes attached to some substratum by means of its three adhesive papillae, on which it stands in an upside down posture. In this attached

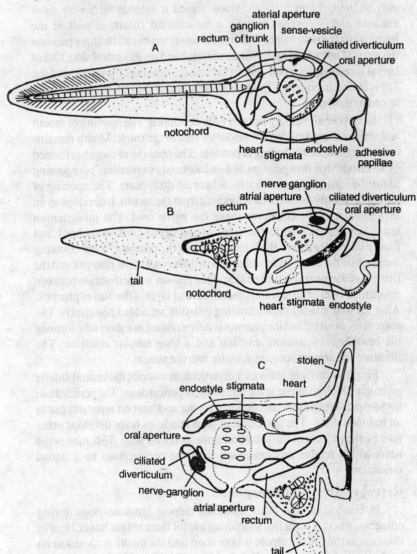

Fig. 2.36. The retrogressive metamorphosis in *Herdmania*.

condition (with the tail upward) the larva undergoes the process of metamorphosis which is of retrogressive type. During the metamorphosis certain advanced characters of the tadpole larva starts degenerating and adult appears as degenerated form. Such advanced structures are poorly developed in adult and may remain there in vestigeal form.

Following changes have been taking place during metamorphosis :

1. First of all the tail of larva begins to reduce and finally the entire tail disappears. The reduction and disappearance of tail takes place partly by resorption and partly due to casting. Resorption of tail is done by a process of phagocytosis.

2. Transparent test is secreted by the ectodermal epithelium.

3. Nerve cord, notochord, muscles, endodermal strands and fins also disappear during metamorphosis.

4. Four ectodermal ampullae are formed by ectodermal layer at four corners grows out forming prominent out growths. Test is also pushed by the out growths. These ampullae provide additional adhesion for attachment. They are also helpful in respiration. After sometime two more, similar, but smaller ampullae appear in dorsolateral side. Towards the end of metamorphosis the adhesive papillae and the ectodermal ampullae disappear and the test develops the foot to fix the animal more firmly to the objects.

5. The number of gill-slits or stigmata increases. The pharynx itself increases in size to form the branchial sac.

6. Stomach and intestine become longer and the appearance of lobes of liver can also be seen.

7. Atrial and branchial siphons are developed at their respective apertures by the invagination of test.

8. Except visceral ganglion, the entire nervous system starts degenerating. The ocelli and otocyst which are developed in larva also disappeared. The visceral ganglion persists even in adult but some workers believe that even visceral ganglion disappears during metamorphosis and the adult nerve ganglion and neural gland are formed a new by proliferation of cells from the wall of neural duct.

9. At the same time when these changes are taking place the portion between mouth and the point of attachment grows very rapidly. This growth brings about a dorso-posterior rotation of the body by nearly 180 degrees. This rotation brings the atriopore and branchiopore at the free distal end of the body.

10. Gonads and vascular system are developed from the mesodermal cells of tadpole larva.

It is clear from the above account that the active. free swimming larva with well developed sense organs. nervous system and notochord etc. changes into *fixed* and *inert* adult. Thus all the basic chordate characters (notochord, dorsal tubular nerve cord and the gill-slits) are lost except the gill-slits. Thus the adult ascidian does not at all appear as a chordate. This type of metamorphosis in which the adult, instead of acquiring advanced characters, looses them, becoming a degenerate form is called *retrogressive metamorphosis.*

AFFINITIES OF UROCHORDATE

The systemic position of Urochordata has long been a controversial issue. For the first time *Aristotle* described a simple ascidian under the name *Tethyum. Lamarck* (1816) coined the term Tunicata and placed them between Radiata and Vermes. *Cuvier* (1817) classified them along with Mollusca, *Milne Edwards* (1843) formed a new class Molluscoidea to include Bryozoa, Polyzoa and Tunicata. *Kowalevsky* (1886) described the development of a simple ascidian and included tunicates under phylum Chordata.

Affinities with non-chordates

It shows several non-chordate characters :

1. Sessile nature like poriferans and coelenterates.
2. Mechanism of filter feeding and respiration.
3. Budding chain of new zooids.
4. Presence of eye and otocyst in the larva.
5. Presence of typhlosole in the intestine.

However, none of the above characters are very convincing, therefore, the relationship between urochordates and non- chordates is doubtful.

Affinities with chordates

Following are the chordate characters of Ascidian tadpole larva:

1. Presence of dorsal tubular nerve cord.
2. A conspicuous notochord is present.
3. Presence of gill-slits in the pharyngeal wall.

Thus the chordate affinities of urochordates is beyond any doubt.

Affinities with hemichordates

It shows following similarities with *Balanoglossus*:

1. In both the pharynx is perforated by branchial apertures.
2. Development of nervous system almost resembles in both.
3. Occurence of restricted notochord.

Dissimilarities

1. Ascidian are free swimming or fixed while *Balanoglossus* is tubicolous.
2. Body of *Balanoglossus* is divisible into proboscis, collar and trunk but in ascidians it is compact.
3. Notochord is present only in the tail region of ascidian tadpole larva while the nature of stomochord is doubtful in *Balanoglossus*.

Affinities with Cephalochordates

Adult tunicates are related to *Amphioxus* on the following characters:

1. Food concentration mechanism is similar in both.
2. Mechanism of respiration is similar.
3. Endostyle and associated parts are similar in both.
4. The velar tentacle of *Amphioxus* are similar to the branchial tentacles of *Herdmania*.
5. Atrium also develops in both.

Besides adult similarities the tadpole larva of *Herdmania* also shows striking similarities with adult *Amphioxus*:

1. Presence of dorsal and central fins.
2. Presence of endostyle.
3. Atrial complex similar.
4. Presence of notochord.
5. Identical early stages of development.
6. Presence of otocyst in both.
7. Single median eye is present.
8. Dorsal tubular nerve cord is present in both.

Dissimilarities

Though a number of similarities exist between them, however, following dissimilarities are seen in both.

1. The notochord and nerve cord absent in adult *Herdmania* while present in *Amphioxus*.
2. The coelom is absent in *Herdmania*.
3. A body covering i.e. test is present in *Herdmania* but absent in *Amphioxus*.
4. Liver and heart are present in *Herdmania*.
5. They are bisexual and the metamorphosis of larva is retrogressive in *Herdmania*.

Affinities with vertebrates

The urochordates are also related to the vertebrates.

1. The tadpole larva can be compared with a larval fish.
2. Presence of dorsal tubular nervous system, notochord and pharyngeal gill-slits in tadpole.
3. Neural gland of adult can be compared with the pituitary of vertebrates.
4. Endostyle is homologous with thyroid gland of vertebrate.
5. Typhlosole in the ascidian intestine is comparable to the spiral valve of elasmobranch intestine.
6. Muscular postanal tail with tail fins.

Conclusion

Regarding the ancestry of urochordates, it is evident that they are primitive and degenerate ancestral to chordate. *Willey* (1894) was the opinion that the tadpole larva of ascidian is a relic of part free-swimming chordate ancestor while the adults are regarded to be secondary sessile and degenerate to such an extent that they have become adapted to sessile life. The tadpole larva is regarded to represent the ancestor of chordate.

Revision Questions

1. Classify urochordata giving characters and examples of each order.
2. Write short notes on : (a) *Botryllus,* (b) *Ciona,* (c) *Clavellina.*
3. Give in detail the internal anatomy of *Herdmania.*
4. Draw a neat and labelled diagram of alimentary canal of *Herdmania.* Describe the mode of feeding in it.
5. Describe in detail the structure of pharynx in *Herdmania* and also describe the mode of feeding.
6. Describe the blood vascular system and course of blood circulation in *Herdmania.*
7. Describe the excretory organs of *Herdmania.*
8. Discuss the affinities of *Herdmania.*
9. Write short notes on : (a) Dorsal tubercle. (b) Neural gland complex. (c) Retrogressive metamorphosis. (d) Endostyle. (e) Test or tunics.

Amphioxus (Branchiostoma)

It is a small group of little fish-like animals with only two genera and a dozen species.

Characters of Subphylum Cephalochordata

1. Body is adapted for burrowing and swimming.
2. Body is without paired appendages. Median unpaired dorsal, ventral and caudal fins are present.
3. Body is differentiated into trunk and tail only.
4. Body wall is single layered without any exoskeleton.
5. Dorsal muscles are very thick and segmentally arranged.
6. Notochord extends the entire length of body.
7. True enterocoelous coelom is present.
8. Respiration occurs by diffusion through general body surface and gill-slits.
9. Circulatory system closed, heart is absent. Respiratory pigment is absent. Corpuscles are few.
10. Excretion by protonephridia.
11. Nervous system is built on vertebrate plan comprising central, peripheral and autonomic nervous system.
12. Sexes are separate. Gonads are several and segmentally present without gonoducts. Fertilization external, development indirect with a larval stage.

Classification

Sub-phylum includes a single class Leptocardii which has a single family Branchiostomidae. This family contains only two genera *Branchiostoma* (*Amphioxus*) and *Asymmetron*

AMPHIOXUS

Phylum	-	Chordata
Group	-	Protochordata
Sub-phylum	-	Cephalochordata
Class	-	Leptocardii
Genus	-	*Amphioxus* or *Branchiostoma.*
Species	-	*lanceolatum.*

Cephalochordata is a small group of fish-like lanceolates commonly known as *Amphioxus. Pallas* (1778) first discovered the genus *Branchiostoma lanceolatum.* He considers it to be a slug and named as *Limax lanceolatum* in his description. Later on *O.G. Costa* (1834) identified correctly and named as *Branchiostoma* on the basis of perforated pharynx. Name *Amphioxus* was given by *Yarrel* (1836). *Muller* (1841) described it in details.

There are about nine species of *Branchiostoma* which are cosmopolitan in distribution and abundantly found in Japan where the natives use them as food . *Dolichobranchus indicus* is a recently investigated species of the group.

Habits and Habitat

It is a marine animal commonly occurring on the sandy shores of the temperate subtropical and tropical oceans of the world. It is littoral and never descends below fifty fathoms. It leads a dual life. It is buried in the sand in an upright condition with only the oral hood protruding out. During dim-light it comes out the burrow and swims swiftly by lateral undulation of the body. According to *Newman* the *Amphioxus* swims occasionally when it is disturbed. It drives back into the sandy bottom and by s triking the noto-chordal process against the substratum it finds out another spot for its burrow. It is ciliary feeder and feeds on microscopic organisms in the plankton. Sexes are separate but there is no sexual dimorphism. Fertilization is external, development is indirect with a larval stage. The larva grows into adult within three months.

EXTERNAL MORPHOLOGY

Shape, size and colour

The body is elongated, semi-transparent, laterally compressed and flexible. It measures about 5-7 cm in length. The colour of the body is dark red or reddish brown. It superficially resembles to a small fish.

Division of body

The body of *Amphioxus* is divided into two regions, the *trunk* and

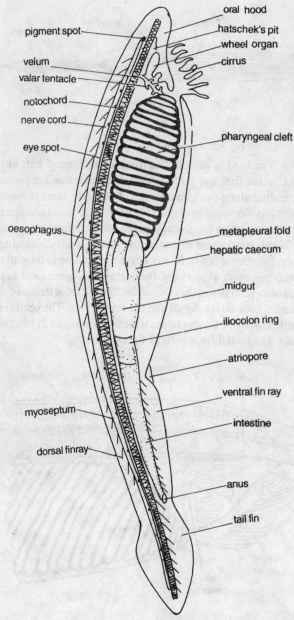

oral hood

pigment spot

hatschek's pit

wheel organ

cirrus

velum

valar tentacle

notochord

nerve cord

eye spot

pharyngeal cleft

oesophagus

metapleural fold

hepatic caecum

midgut

iliocolon ring

atriopore

ventral fin ray

myoseptum

intestine

dorsal finray

anus

tail fin

Fig. 3.1. *Amphioxus.*

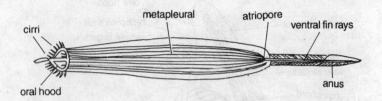

Fig. 3.2. *Amphioxus*. Ventral view.

tail or *caudal*. The head is absent. The trunk is the longest part of the
body. It lacks paired fins, but three unpaired median fins are present.
Dorsally, extending along the whole length of the body, there is *median
dorsal fin*, which is supported by about 250-300 *fin-ray boxes* arranged in
one row. The fin-ray boxes are slightly tough and rectangular in shape.
The fin-ray boxes are pockets of connective tissue, each containing a
central nodule. Number of dorsal fin ray boxes has nothing to do with the
number of body segments. Posteriorly, the dorsal fin is continuous as the
tail fin and postero-ventrally as the *ventral fin*. The tail fin is flattened and
equally expanded both on the dorsal and the ventral side. The ventral fin
is also supported by 30-50 fin-ray boxes which are arranged in two rows
(right and left). The caudal-fin is without fin-ray boxes.

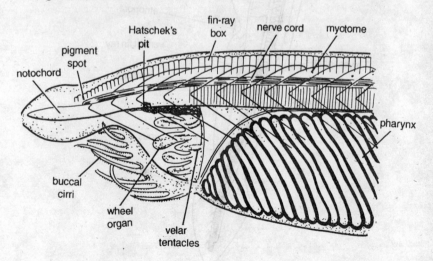

Fig. 3.3. *Amphioxus*. Anterior end.

Trunk bears three openings: the *mouth, atriopore* and *anus.* The mouth is very wide and lies at the anterior end of the trunk over hung by the *rostrum.* It leads into the *oral hood* formed by dorsal and lateral projections of the body. The edge of the oral hood is provided with 10 to 11 pairs of *oral cirri* or *buccal tentacles.* The cirri help in filter feeding and for the indrawal of water currents towards the pharynx. The atriopore is a small mid-ventral aperture situated infront of the ventral fin. Through this aperture the *atrium* opens out which surrounds the pharynx. The anus lies at the base of caudal-fin on the ventral side slightly to the left side of the median line.

From behind the oral-hood and continuous with its lateral edges arise a pair of *metapleural folds.* These run all along the ventral surface of the anterior two-third of the body, and meet just in front of the ventral fin around the *atriopore.* Metapleural folds are in fact projecting edges of the dorso-lateral wall that encloses the atrium.

BODY WALL

The body wall consists of *skin, muscles* and *peritoneum.*

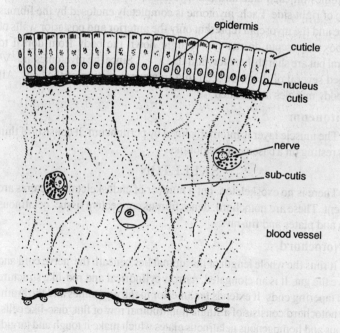

Fig. 3.4. *Amphioxus.* V.S. of body wall.

Skin

The skin consists of an outer thin *epidermis* and *dermis* or *cutis*.

The epidermis is made up of a single layer of columnar epithelial cells resting on a *basement membrane*. In the larva it is ciliated but adults are devoid of cilia. In adults a thin layer of non-pigmented *cuticle* is present out side the epidermis. The cuticle is secreted by epidermal cells. Scattered between the epidermal cells are unicellular gland cells and sensory cells.

The cutis is differentiated into an outer *fibrous layer* and an inner *sub-cutis*. The cutis lies beneath the epidermis and it is tough, thin and compact. The sub-cutis is made up of gelatinous matrix containing blood vessels, nerve fibres etc.

Musculature

The muscles lie just beneath the skin. They are very thick in dorso-lateral regions. The muscles are divided up by tough partitions of *fibrous cutis*, into a series of segmental blocks called *myotomes* or *myomeres*, the partitions are called *myosepta* or *myocommata*.There are about 60 myotomes on each side and the myotomes of left side alternates with those of right side. Each myotome is completely enclosed by the fibrous tissue and the myosepta represent only the anterior and posterior walls of the box. Myosepta do not run straight down the body from dorsal to ventral but are sharply bent forward like a '>' . Since the myotomes are 'V' shaped several of them are seen in a transverse section of the body. All the body muscles are striated.

Peritoneum

The muscle layer is internally lined by peritoneum. It consists of thin cells resting on a basement membrane.

SKELETON

There is no exoskeleton, but a number of endoskeletal structures are present. These are notochord, dense fibrous connective tissue, gelatinous rods and plates and fin-rays.

1. Notochord

It runs the whole length of the animal lies beneath the nerve cord and above the gut. It is an elongated, narrow cylindrical and rod-like structure with tapering ends. It extends far anterior to the myotomes and the brain. The notochord consists of a single longitudinal row of flat, disc-like cells. fibrous and homogenous gelatinous plates which make it tough and turgid. A fluid fills the spaces between these cells. The row of cells is enclosed by a thin, elastic membrane known as *elastica interna* which is surrounded by a thick layar of fibrous connective tissue called the *notochordal sheath*.

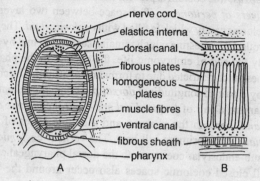

Fig. 3.5. *Amphioxus*. T.S. of notochord and L.S. of notochord.

The function of notochord is to prevent shortening of the body when the longitudinal muscles contract.

2. Dense fibrous connective tissue

This tissue provides firmness to the body by filling up spaces between its organs. It surrounds the myotomes, notochord and nerve cord where it forms a sort of neural canal and neural spine.

3. Gelatinous rods and plates

Gelatinous rods support the gill-bars of the pharynx, oral cirri and free edges of the oral hood. The endostyle is supported by gelatinous plates.

4. Fin-ray boxes

The fin ray boxes support the dorsal and ventral fins.

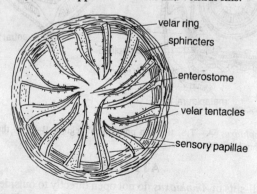

Fig. 3.6. *Amphioxus*. Velum.

COELOM

In *Amphioxus*, true coelom is present which is lined with *somatic* and *splanchnic layers of peritoneum.* The space between two layers is the coelom or coelomic cavity which is filled with *coelomic fluid.* The coelom is spacious around the intestine which remains suspended in it by a dorsal mesentery. By the end of embryonic life, the coelom in the pharyngeal region becomes much restricted due to formation of atrium. The coelom is represented by a pair of longitudinal *dorsal pharyngeal coelomic canal* above the pharynx, a pair of *longitudinal mid-ventral coelomic canal* or *endostylar canal* beneath the pharynx and a double series of *vertical coelomic canals* in the primary gill-bars. The *vertical coelomic canals* connect the sub-endostylar coelom with the dorsal pharyngeal coelomic canals. Small closed coelomic spaces also occur around the mid-gut diverticulum and in the gonads (gonocoel).

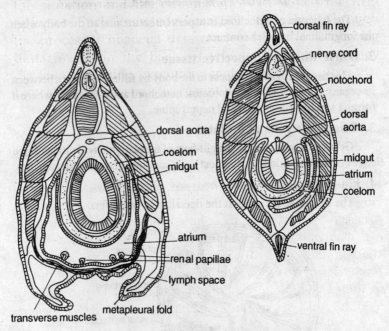

Fig. 3.7. *Amphioxus.* A—T.S. through pharyngeal region, B—T.S. through body behind atriopore.

ATRIUM

The gill-slits of *Amphioxus* do not open directly to outside but into a special chamber called *atrium* which is lined with ectoderm (ectodermal in origin). It is situated in the lateral extensions of the body wall, the *metapleural folds.* The right and left metapleural folds are connected with each other by a transverse shelf called the *epiplure* which encloses the pharynx anteriorly and laterally, and the anterior part of the intestine. The atrium opens out through the *atriopore* situated infront of the anus. Posteriorly, the atrium further extends behind the *atriopore* as a blind pouch on the right side of the intestine upto the anus. A pair of blind pockets arise from a point on the lateral margin of the pharynx. These are called *brown funnels.* They are forwardly directed in the dorsal coelomic canals and are also called the *atrio-coelomic canals.* Their function is unknown.

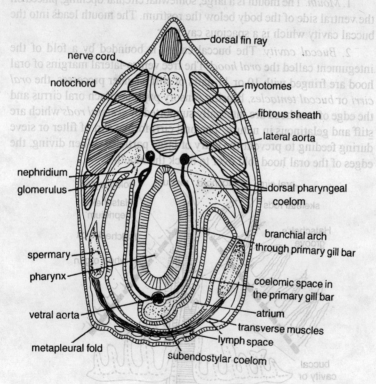

Fig. 3.8. *Amphioxus.* T.S. through middle region.

DIGESTIVE SYSTEM

The digestive system consists of *alimentary canal* and *digestive glands.*

Alimentary canal

The alimentary canal is a straight tube and consists of following zones:

I. The Ingressive zone

II. The Progressive zone

III. The Degressive zone

IV. The Egressive zone

I. The Ingressive zone

The ingressive zone comprises the *mouth* and the *buccal cavity.*

1. *Mouth.* The mouth is a large, somewhat circular opening, placed on the ventral side of the body below the rostrum. The mouth leads into the buccal cavity which is a spacious cavity.

2. *Buccal cavity.* The buccal cavity is bounded by a fold of the integument called the *oral hood.* The free ventro-lateral margins of oral hood are fringed with 10 or 11 pairs of stiff, slender processes, the *oral cirri* or *buccal tentacles,* bearing sensory papillae. Each oral cirrus and the edge of oral hood are internally supported by *skeletal rods* which are stiff and gelatinous in nature. The oral cirri form a sort of filter or sieve during feeding to prevent the entry of large particles. When diving, the edges of the oral hood fold over to block the mouth.

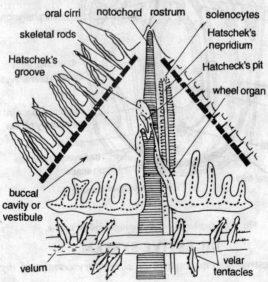

Fig. 3.9. *Amphioxus.* Dorsal wall of oral hood.

The buccal cavity or vestibule is shallow and possesses a complex set of ciliated and grooved processes is known as *Muller's organ* or *wheel organ* or *rotatory organ*. The epithelium of wheel organ is folded to form six or eight finger-like processes with a median groove. The mid-dorsal process is largest and displaced a little to the left. It bears a glandular ciliated groove called the *Hatschek's groove* terminating into the *Hatschek's pit* which is small depression. It secretes mucous. The buccal cavity or vestibule is bounded behind by a muscular membrane, the *velum* which separates it from the pharynx and is perforated by an aperture, the *enterostome*. The enterostome has been sometimes called the true mouth and is the actual opening which formed the mouth in the larva. The velum on its posterior border has a circlet of twelve backwardly directed *velar tentacles*. The tentacles are covered with numerous sensory papillae. The general surface of these organs is ciliated. Tentacles prevent large particles from entering the mouth.

II. Progressive zone

The progressive zone of alimentary canal includes the pharynx and oesophagus.

1. *Pharynx.* It is the largest part of alimentary canal which occupies about two-third part of the body. It is laterally compressed sac and remains suspended in the atrial or peribranchial cavity which surrounds it from all sides except on dorsal side. The pharynx is divided into two parts : a short *prebranchial chamber* and a large *branchial chamber*.

The branchial chamber is perforated by 180-250 oblique vertical gill-slits. The two adjacent gill-slits are separated by the median *gill cleft*.

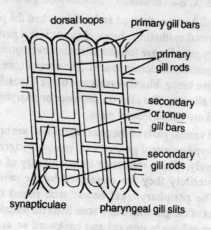

Fig. 3.10. Side wall of pharynx.

Each gill cleft is supported by skeletal rod. The number of gill-slits in young one is much less but their number is increased by further subdivision of previous slits. The division is effected by the downward growth from the drosal wall of the gill-slits which is termed as *tongue bar*. The original gill-slits are therefore called the *primary gill bars* while the latter sub-divided gill-slits are known as *secondary gill-slits* and supported by *secondary gill bars*. Thus the secondary gill bars alternate with the primary gill bars. The primary and secondary gill bars are interconnected by cross-bars, the *synapticulae*. The gill bars and synapticulae are supported by *skeletal rods*, the rods of the primary bars are forked at their ventral extremities while the rods of secondary bars are not forked. The synapticulae also contain the skeletal rods.

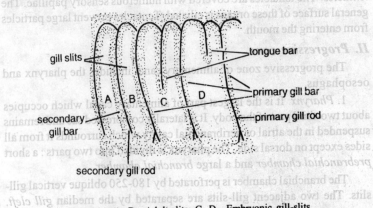

Fig. 3.11. A, B—Adult-slits; C, D—Embryonic gill-slits.

The primary gill bars are formed at the time when the pharynx was bounded by the parietal epithelium, hence they enclose a part of coelom. While the secondary gill-slits are formed after the development of atrium so that they do not possess coelomic spaces. The central core of gill bar is filled with connective tissue, blood vessels and nerve fibres. The gill bars are lined with cilia all over. The cilia on the inner or pharyngeal side are especially long and are called *frontal cilia*.

The dorsal and ventral parts of the pharyngeal wall are not perforated and constitute *hyperpharyngeal groove* and *hypopharyngeal groove* or *endostyle* respectively. These terminate independently of one another posteriorly but anteriorly they are connected by the *peripharyngeal ciliated bands*. The peripharyngeal bands arch round the pharynx immediately infront of the gill slits. They arise from the anterior end of the endostyle, they run obliquely upward and backward so as to meet the anterior end of hyperpharyngeal groove. The hyperpharyngeal groove is also known as *epipharyngeal groove* is a prominent ciliated groove present as on the mid-dorsal line. Posteriorly it runs upto oesophagus.

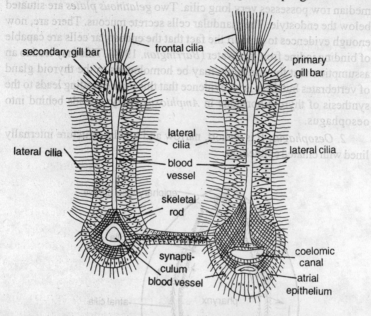

Fig. 3.12. *Amphioxus*. T.S. of primary and secondary gill-bars.

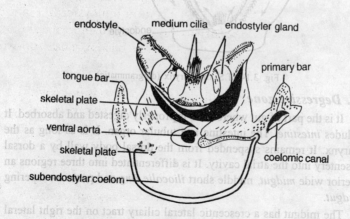

Fig. 3.13. *Amphioxus*. T.S. of Endostyle.

The hypopharyngeal groove or endostyle runs mid-ventrally upto oesophagus. It is lined with four longitudinal tracts of glandular cells which are separated from each other due to presence of ciliary cells. The median row possesses very long cilia. Two *gelatinous plates* are situated below the endostyle. The glandular cells secrete mucous. There are, now enough evidences to support the fact that the endostylar cells are capable of binding iodine from sea water (*Barrington,* 1964). This may lead to an assumption that the endostyle may be homologous to the thyroid gland of vertebrates but there is no evidence that this iodine binding leads to the synthesis of thyroid hormone in *Amphioxus.* Pharynx leads behind into oesophagus.

2. *Oesophagus.* It is a short, narrow and tubular structure internally lined with ciliated epithelium.

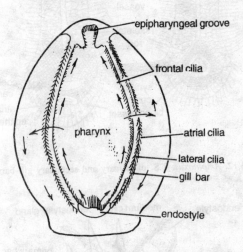

Fig. 3.14. T.S. of pharynx (diagrammatic).

III. Degressive zone

It is the part of gut where food is properly digested and absorbed. It includes *intestine.* The intestine is a tubular organ. It is as long as the pharynx. It remains suspended from the dorsal body wall by a dorsal mesentery into the atrial cavity. It is differentiated into three regions an anterior wide *midgut,* middle short *iliocolic ring* and posterior tapering *hindgut.*

The midgut has a crescentic lateral ciliary tract on the right lateral side. The cilia of lateral ciliary tract beat downward towards a groove that starts within the *midgut diverticulum*. The midgut diverticulum arises from the junction of oesophagus and midgut. The midgut follows the iliocolic ring. which is heavily ciliated. Its cilia beat backwards and downwards on the left side, and forwards and upwards on the right side. The ciliary action rotates the mucous cord containing the food.

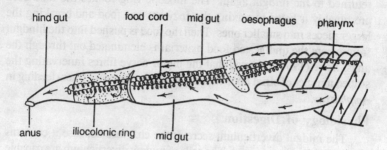

Fig. 3.15. *Amphioxus*. Food current.

The hindgut has a dorsal ciliated groove that starts from the iliocolic ring and extends posteriorly.

IV. Egressive zone

The posterior most part of the hindgut is heavily ciliated and may be termed as *rectum*. The rectum opens out through a small circular aperture, the *anus*. The anus is situated at the base of caudal fin on the vertral side. It has *anal sphincter.*

Food and feeding

The food of *Amphioxus* consists of micro-organisms like diatoms, protozoans and other organic particles etc. The animal does not usually swim about in search of food, but most of the time it remains in its burrow with its anterior end projecting in water. A continuous current of water is maintained due to well set movement of the cilia of gill-slits. The water enters in through the mouth and after taking its course through vestibule, enterostome, pharynx, gill-slits and atrium comes out through atriopore. Thus the animal is ciliary feeder. In feeding the oral cirri are turned inwards over the entrance of oral hood. Thus. bigger particles of sand are excluded from water entering the mouth. The food particles suspended in the water are detained and collected in pharynx. These food particles entangled into mucous sheet secreted by glandular cells of endostyle. These mucous sheets are passed dorsally by the lateral branchial cilia on to the inner faces of the gill-bars and then to the epipharyngeal groove by the beating of frontal branchial cilia. The mucous sheet on reaching the dorsal side in the groove is rolled by the ciliary action and gradually pushed into oesophagus. From the oesophagus the food is directed towards the lumen of the midgut diverticulum which is also a ciliated structure internally. Here digestive enzymes are mixed with the food materials. The food is returned to the midgut again. The iliocolic ring rotates the food cord presumably it helps in mixing the enzymes and food and breaking the larger pieces into smaller ones. Then the food is pushed into the hindgut from where the undigested food material is eleminated out through the anus. *Bone* (1960) reported that the motor nerve fibres innervating the striped muscles of atrial floor control the whole process of filter-feeding in *Amphioxus*.

Physiology of Digestion

The midgut diverticulum secretes the enzymes because it contains zymogen cells (*Barrington*). The cells of midgut diverticulum are capable of phagocytosis, thus intra-cellular digestion occurs. The extra-cellular digestion takes place in the midgut. The digestive juice contains *amylase*, *lipase* and *protease enzymes*. Complete digestion occurs in the absence of acid. The hindgut absorbs the digested food.

Respiration

The respiratory organs are not of special type in *Amphioxus*. The pharynx besides digestive function is also specialised for respiration by gills. The gill-bars are richly supplied with blood vessels and their thin walls are able to exchange gases. But it is doubtful whether pharynx helps in oxygenation of blood or not because in the blood there is no respiratory pigment. According to *Orton*, the main function of the pharynx is the filteration of food particles. The gill-bars consume a lot of oxygen for operating their cilia during feeding movements. Now it is regarded that the exchange of gases takes place in the wall of atrium, in the metapleural folds and the general body surface.

BLOOD VASCULAR SYSTEM

The blood vascular system is simple in *Amphioxus*. It is of *closed type*. The heart is absent and the blood is colourless due to absence of respiratory pigment. Thus the circulatory system is mainly responsible for transportation of food materials and waste products rather for exchange of oxygen and carbon dioxide. The blood vessels are few, simple and without any structural distinction of arteries and veins except few. The system of blood-vessels is fundamentally similar to that of vertebrates. The main vessels and their branches are as given below :

Sinus venosus

Lying just ventral to the posterior end of the pharynx, there is a small and sac-like structure known as *sinus venosus*. It collects the blood from different parts of body. From sinus venosus, a single longitudinal, *ventral aorta* runs forwards.

Ventral aorta

It is also known as *subendostylar aorta*. It is a median longitudinal vessel that lies beneath the pharynx in the subendostylar coelom. Its walls are muscular and by rhythmical contraction the blood flows in forward direction. In the pharyngeal region the ventral aorta gives off paired branchial arches in the primary gill-bars. These are known as *afferent branchial arteries*.

At the base of each afferent branchial artery there is a swollen ampulla or bulb called *bulbule* or *bulbillus*. The bulbuli are pulsatile functioning as the branchial heart. It helps in carrying the blood in upward direction. The afferent branchial arteries do not break into capillares and leave the pharynx dorsally as *efferent branchial arteries*. The efferent branchial arteries of each side open into lateral dorsal aorta. Before opening into lateral dorsal aorta, each efferent branchial artery breaks up into a small capillary network, the *glomus* near the excretory organ called *nephridium*. The secondary gill-bars also have afferent branchial arteries but they receive blood from the primary gill-bars by means of small *transverse* arteries present in synapticulae.

Dorsal aorta

Two *lateral dorsal aortae,* (the *right* and *left* lateral dorsal aortae) lie one on either side of the epipharyngeal groove. Anteriorly, they continued as the *internal carotid arteries* supplying the blood to the oral hood, wheel organ, oral cirri and dorsally to the Hatschek's nephridium. Dorsally the lateral aortae give off numerous branches that split into capillaries and supply blood to dorsal musculature. In the intestinal region the lateral aortae united to form a main dorsal aorta which lies just beneath the notochord. It gives many branches, the *dorso-intestinal* arteries, to the intestine which form plexus in the intestinal wall. The dorsal aorta continues as *caudal artery* in the tail. In dorsal aorta blood flows in backward direction.

Sub-intestinal vein

It is formed by the union of a *caudal vein,* which collects blood from caudal region, and *lateral intestinal veins,* which receive blood from the

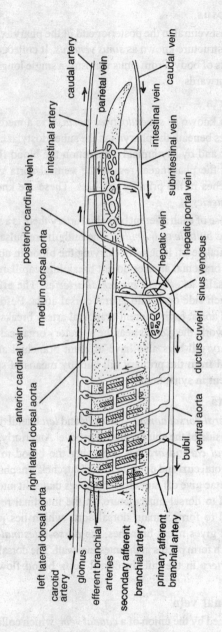

Fig. 3.16. *Amphioxus*. Circulatory system.

plexus of intestinal walls. The sub-intestinal vein lies beneath the intestine. The blood flows in forward direction. This vessel continues anteriorly as *hepatic portal vein* beneath the oesophagus.

Hepatic portal system

The *hepatic portal vein* extends forward along the ventral surface of midgut diverticulum where it breaks up into a capillary network. From midgut diverticulum the blood is collected by a *hepatic vein*. The hepatic vein opens into a small thin walled sac, the *sinus venosus* as described above.

Cardinal veins

The blood from myotomes is returned on either side by an *anterior* and *posterior cardinal veins.* They run laterally in the body wall and unite just behind the pharynx to form a *common cardinal vein* or *ductus cuvieri.* The two ductus cuvieri discharge into the sinus venosus.

Parietal veins

Blood is collected from dorsal body wall by a pair of parietal veins that run above the intestine and then open into the posterior end of sinus venosus.

Course of Circulation

The blood flows in forward direction in the parietal veins, subintestinal vein, posterior cardinal vein and ventral aorta. It flows in backward direction in dorsal aorta and anterior cardinal veins.

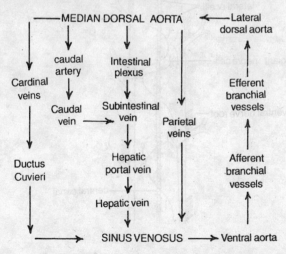

Fig. 3.17. *Amphioxus.* Course of blood circulation.

Blood

Blood of *Amphioxus* is colourless and the red corpuscles are few.
Blood pressure is low.

NERVOUS SYSTEM

The nervous system is similar to that of the vertebrates in fundamental
plan. It is differentiated into as usual three parts: The central nervous
system, the peripheral nervous system and autonomic nervous system.

I. Central Nervous System

It consists of a hollow, tubular dorsal nerve cord which is situated in
mid-dorsal line just above the notochord. It is surrounded with a tough
connective tissue sheath which is continuous with the myocommata as
well as the sheath of notochord. It has no ganglia. Posteriorly, the nerve
cord tapers to a fine point close to the hind end of notochord. Anteriorly,
it terminates abruptly at the level of first myotome only a short way behind
the anterior end of the notochord. A narrow central canal, called *neurocoel*,

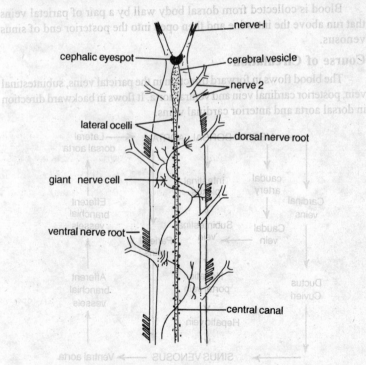

Fig. 3.18. *Amphioxus*. Anterior part of nerve cord.

runs throughout the length of the neural tube. The neurocoel remains filled with *cerebrospinal fluid*. The neurocoel dilates anteriorly so as to form the *cerebral vesicle* without any change in the external diameter of the cord. From the roof of cerebral vesicle a small outgrowth, called the *dorsal diverticulum* arises which extends backwards above the neurocoel. The cerebral vesicle contains two important receptors; a median *pigment spot* in the anterior wall, and a small patch of columnar ciliated cells called the infundibular organ present on the floor of the cerebral vesicle.

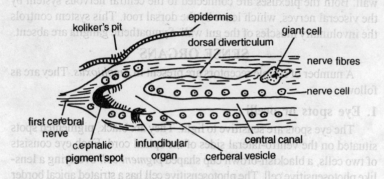

Fig. 3.19. *Amphioxus.* V.S. anterior part of nerve chord.

Histologically, the nerve cord consists of inner *grey matter* of nerve cells which surrounds the neurocoel. The grey matter is surrounded by white matter. At intervals occur very large cells called giant nerve cells connected with nerve fibres of unusual thickness, the *giant nerve fibres*. These giant nerve cells and their fibres coordinate the swimming movements. The giant cells were investigated by *Phode* (1888).

II. Peripheral Nervous System

It comprises the *cerebral nerves* and *spinal nerves*. There are two pairs of cerebral nerves. They lack ventral roots. Both the nerves are anterior to the first myotome and arise by dorsal roots only. The first pair from anterior extremity and the second from dorsal part of the cord. Both pairs of cerebral nerves are sensory in function and carries impulses from the receptors of the snout, oral hood and its cirri to the central nervous system.

The spinal nerves arise in segmental pairs from the dorso-lateral aspects of the nerve cord behind the cerebral vesicle. A *dorsal nerve* arising by a single root from the dorsal aspect of the nerve cord. The *ventral nerve* arising by several separate fibres from the ventral aspect of the nerve cord. The dorsal nerve root is both sensory and motor and passes out to skin between myotomes. The ventral nerve is motor and arises opposite the myotomes which it supplies. The ventral nerves are not enclosed in the neural sheath and do not aggregate in the form of bundle. The dorsal and ventral roots do not join to form mixed spinal nerve as in vertebrates.

III. Autonomic Nervous System

The autonomic nervous system consists of two plexuses in the gut wall. Both the plexuses are connected to the central nervous system by the visceral nerves, which leave by the dorsal root. This system controls the involuntary muscles of the gut wall. Sympathetic ganglia are absent.

SENSE ORGANS

A number of simple receptors are present in *Amphioxus*. They are as follows :

1. Eye spots or ocelli

The eye spots are sensitive to light. They are black, pigmented spots situated on the ventro-lateral sides of the spinal cord. Each eye consists of two cells, a blackish-brown cup shaped *pigment cell* overlying a lens-like photosensitive cell. The photosensitive cell has a striated apical border which serves as a lens. It sends a fine nerve fibre to the nerve cord.

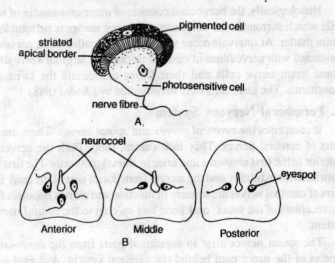

Fig. 3.20. *Amphioxus.* (a) T.S. of spinal chord to show the orientation of eyes (b) Diagram of an eye-spot.

These eyes are oriented in different directions. Even their orientation is not the same on the opposite side. Due to asymmetrical orientation, the direction from which the eyes receive light is different at different parts of the nerve cord, which helps the animal in burrowing in sand or in swimming spirally to perceive light from all the directions.

2. Cephalic pigment spot

The cephalic pigment sport is very large and is situated anteriorly in the wall of cerebral vesicle. A photoreceptor function is attributed to it but since it has no lens or other accessory apparatus. Thus its photosensitive nature is doubtful. Some authors regard it as a thermoreceptor.

3. Infundibular organ

It is a group of tall-ciliated columnar cells in the floor of cerebral vesicle. Its function is still doubtful. According to some workers it is a photoreceptor. Others believe that it helps in the detection of pressure changes (rheo-receptor) of the fluid of neurocoel. More recently, its cells have been proved to be neuro-secretory (homologous to the infundibulum of higher chordates).

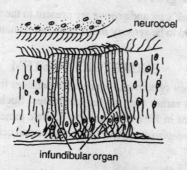

Fig. 3.21. *Amphioxus*. V.S. of infundibular region.

4. Kolliker's pit

It lies on the dorsal side of the cerebral vesicle. It is an invagination of the ectoderm. It marks the area where larval neuropore closes when the adult neural tube is formed. It is considered as chaemoreceptor as it detects the smell of food and water contents.

5. Sensory cells and papillae

The sensory cells are numerous on the dorsal side. Each cell has a sensitive fibril projecting from the general surface of epidermis. The cells are sensitive to the sand particles in which the animal burrows. Some of the cells present on dorsal side of the oral-hood become photosensitive (*Joseph*).

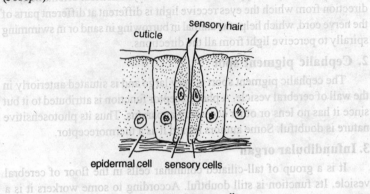

Fig. 3.22. *Sensory cells.*

The oral cirri and velar tentacles are provided with modified sensory papillae which are chaemoreceptor and tactile.

6. Hatschek's groove

The Hatschek's pit and groove are present in the roof of oral hood. It is also considered to be sensory in function but its nature is not definitely known.

EXCRETORY SYSTEM

The excretory system in *Amphioxus* resembles the excretory system of invertebrates rather than higher chordates. Such type of excretory system is present in flatworms and polychaete annelids. The excretory organs are *protonephridia*. Some other organs and cells are also regarded to be excretory.

1. Protonephridia

The protonephridia are ectodermal in origin. There are about 90-100 paired segmental nephridia situated on the lateral surface of the pharynx. Each nephridium is roughly inverted 'L' shaped microscopic structure whose vertical limb is parallel to the primary gill-bar. The vertical limb lies in the coelomic canal of primary gill bar and ends blindly. The upper limb opens into the atrium through an aperture, the *nephridiopore*. The nephridiopore lies against the secondary gill-bar. From dorsal and anterior surface of nephridium numerous short branches arise. Each branch bears the opening of many fine tubules and each tubule ends into a *solenocyte* or *flame cell*. There are about 500 solenocytes in a single protonephridium each measuring about 50μ in length. Each solenocyte bears a nucleus and

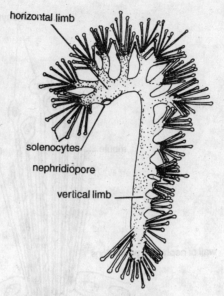

horizontal limb

solenocytes

nephridiopore

vertical limb

Fig. 3.23. *Amhioxus*. Protonephridium.

a long flagellum runs through the tubule. The nephridia are richly supplied with blood vessels and the solenocytes project into the coelomic fluid. The nitrogenous waste products are eliminated from the blood and the coelomic fluid. The waste products are passed into the atrium through the nephridiopores and finally to out side through the atriopore.

2. Hatscheck's nephridium

It is also a large, narrow tube-like structure resembling the nephridia. It is situated on the left and ventral side of the notochord in the region of oral-hood. Posteriorly it opens into the pharynx just behind the velum, whereas anteriorly it ends blindly just infront of Hatschek's groove. Along its whole length it receives solenocytes which are surrounded with a coelomic sac.

3. Renal papillae

The renal papillae are small groups of columnar epithelial cells on the floor of the atrium. Their excretory function is not well known.

4. Brown funnels

These are large tube-like structures present on the dorsal side of the pharynx near the posterior end. Their wide posterior ends open into the

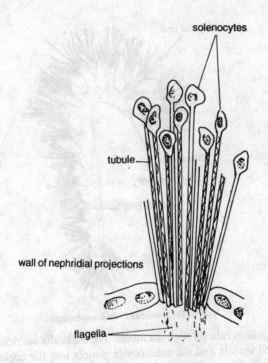

solenocytes

tubule

wall of nephridial projections

flagella

Fig. 3.24. *Amphioxus.* A solenoyte.

atrium where as their narrow anterior ends open into the dorsal coelomic canals. These funnels are lined with columnar cells containing brown pigment supposed to be excretory products.

REPRODUCTIVE SYSTEM

The sexes are separate in *Amphioxus* but there is no sexual dimorphism. The adult bears 26-27 pairs of similar goands metamerically arranged in two rows from 25-51 segments. This region of the body is known as *branchio-genital region.* The goands are simple hollow sacs of mesodermal in origin and building conspicuously into the atrial cavity. They are covered externally by the body wall and internally by the atrial epithelium. Each gonad later acquires a central cavity. the *primary gonadial cavity* and also become surrounded by a *secondary gonadial cavity* or *gonocoel.*

The gonads are without gonoducts and their products i.e. sperms or ova are discharged by the rupture of the gonadial membrane. The apertures by which they escape close and later on the gonads develop a fresh.

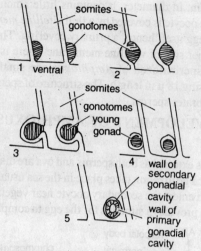

Fig. 3.25. *Amphioxus*. Development of gonads.

Breeding Season

Breeding season of *Amphioxus* is in the late spring and early summer. The male and female emerge out of their burrows and the gametes are liberated through the atriopore into the sea water where fertilization takes place.

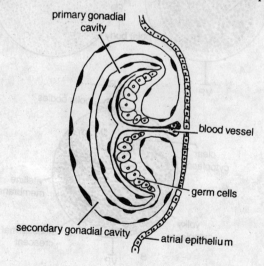

Fig. 3.26. *Amphioxus*. V.S. of mature gonad.

The eggs are released in secondary oocyte stage which are small measuring 0.12 mm. in diameter. It contains little amount of yolk i.e. *microlecithal*. The oocyte is covered by a thin *vitelline membrane* which is secreted by the egg itself hence, a primary covering. The perivitelline membrane lies inner side of vitelline membrane. There is no secondary membrane. The spermatozoa of *Amphioxus* are smallest amongst vertebrates measuring 18 μ in length. The structure of sperm is similar to that of other vertebrates sperms.

DEVELOPMENT OF AMPHIOXUS

Fertilization

Fertilization is external as both sperms and ova are discharged by the respective parents. Fertilization takes place in the sea usually at about the sun set. The sperm enters the secondary oocyte near vegetal pole and the entry of the sperm provides a stimulus for the egg to complete the second

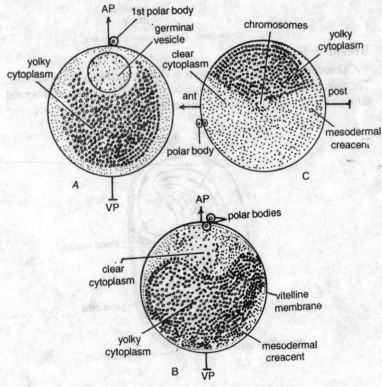

Fig. 3.27. *Amphioxus*. Egg before fertilization.

maturation division. Second polar body develops by the second maturation division which comes to lie near the animal pole just within the vitelline membrane. The sperm enters the egg near vegetal pole where the perivitelline membrane remains longest in a fluid conditions. As soon as the sperm has reached the egg itself, however, the toughening of this membrane is rapidly completed. In the mean time the space between egg and the original membrane is filled and both the membranes fuse to form the *fertilization membrane*.

The entrance of the sperm causes the second meiotic division to become completed and thus the second polar body is developed. After the entrance of sperm the head enlarges and becomes equal in size to the egg nucleus. The two nuclei then meet and fuse in the usual manner. The point of fusion is lying just a little above the equator of the egg and slightly toward the side which will eventually be the posterior of the embryo.

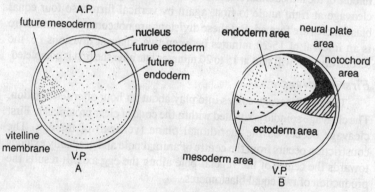

Fig. 3.28. *Amphioxus.* Showing the fate map.

Changes in the egg contents after fertilization and fate map. Just after fertilization presumptive areas are developed by the rearrangement of the cytoplasmic portions in the egg. At the animal pole an area of *clear cytoplasm* is developed by the repture of the germinal vesicle. In the mean time the *granular peripheral cytoplasm* flows downwards towards the vegetal pole and eventually condensed to form a *crescent shaped area* at the future posterior end. At this stage the egg attains bilateral symmetry. It has been observed that various cytoplasmic areas give rise to definite structure in the embryo. The different types of cytoplasm of these area are called *organ forming substances* or *organ specific areas*. During segmentation or cleavage these substances or areas migrate in an orderly fashion to the various blastomeres and from here to the definite regions of the embryo. It has been observed and proved that *ectoderm* of the organism is developed from the clear areas of animal pole while *endoderm* is derived from the yolky cells of vegetal pole and *mesoderm* is formed from the crescent of granular cytoplasm.

Cleavage

Cleavage being the process of segmentation of one-celled zygote into many celled blastula, is a quick process which starts soon after the fertilization has taken place roughly at sun-set and is completed till early morning. The vitelline membrane of the egg before the process starts, gets separated from the ooplasm and a wide cavity appears round the ooplasm. Where there is less amount of yolk, there is holoblastic cleavage i.e. equal and complete. Here the entire egg is divided into equal and identical blastomers by the first vertical furrow running from pole to pole through middle of the mesodermal crescent. The first cleavage is followed by second cleavage at right angle to first, again by vertical furrow so four equal blastomeres are formed. But these divisions are not continuous and there is an interval of 15-20 minutes between two adjacent divisions i.e. the second division will start at 15 to 20 minutes late after the first is completed.

First Cleavage

The first cleavage comes into play about an hour after fertilization. The cleavage spindle is situated within the cone of clear protoplasm. First cleavage occurs on the meridional plane (vertical) of the egg. The constriction occurs from the centre of animal pole and gradually extends towards the centre of the vegetal pole along the egg axis. It results the production of two equal blastomeres.

Second Cleavage

The second cleavage, being next to first is late by half an hour. The second furrow is also vertical but is at right angle to the first. But it is not exactly in the middle so the posterodorsal pair of blastomeres is slightly larger than the posteroventral pair.

Third Cleavage

The second cleavage is followed by third furrow after an interval of about 15 minutes. This cleavage is not vertical but horizontal at right angle to the first two furrows. It is not equatorial but slightly nearer to the animal pole as a result of which eight cells are formed four are smaller and other four are larger. The smaller cells at the animal pole are called the *micromeres* whereas the rest at vegetative pole are *macromeres*. With respect to the orientation of these blastomeres to the future embryo, the upper pair of micromeres may be recognised as anterior while lower pair as ventral. Similarly, upper pair of macromeres is dorsal while lower pair posterior. Moreover, it is also noticed that anterior pair of micromeres and the dorsal pair of macromeres are comparatively slightly larger than the other pairs of their own type. Likely it may be noted that the potential ectodermial material is mainly present in micromeres the potential endodermial substances in the dorsal macromeres and dorsal parts of posterior macromeres and that of mesodermal in the two posterior macromeres.

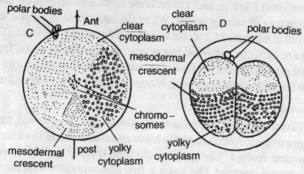

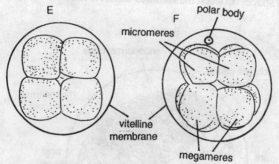

Fig. 3.29. Early cleavage.

Fourth Cleavage

The fourth cleavage appears about 15 minutes after the third cleavage is completed. The fourth cleavage furrows are two in number and are meridional. All the 8 cells divide to form 16 cells of which 8 are micromeres and the other eight are macromeres.

Fifth Cleavage

The fifth cleavage appears after fourth cleavage with an interval of 15 to 20 minutes. This cleavage is double and horizontal so that 32 cells are formed within four tiers-two tiers of micromeres and two of macromeres.

Sixth Cleavage

The sixth cleavage appears after fifth cleavage with an interval of 15 to 20 minutes. This cleavage is vertical and results in doubling of the blastomeres so that 64 cells in total are resulted.

Blastulation

The term *morula* can be applied for the solid ball of dividing cells specially at 16 celled stage. As already told above that 6th cleavage results in the formation of 64 cells, and 128 cells are formed by seventh division and the regularity of timing is lost. When the embryonic mass is about four hour old it consists of 256 cells and is diagramatic *blastula*. The blastula is not perfectly spherical but is pear shaped when viewed from the side, the pointed end being posterior, and is made of a single layer of cells which are arranged about a large *blastocoel*, filled with a watery fluid.

Formation of Blastocoel

The formation of blastocoel actually starts from four celled stage during segmentation. At this stage the blastomeres are rounded and hence not in complete contact. The space in question is filled with blastocoel jelly or gelatinous material. The space at first communicates with the out side through spaces between the rounded cells. As the cleavage proceeds,

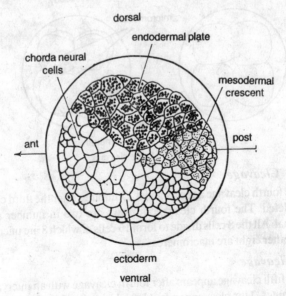

Fig. 3.30. The blastula.

the openings into the blastocoel are closed by the adhesion of cells at their inner ends. In the meantime the blastula greatly increases in size as the jelly of blastocoel absorbs water and becomes quite fluid. This fluid pushes the cells outward around it and blastomeres arrange in a single layer around blastocoel.

Rearrangement of organ forming substances during blastulation

The arrangement of inner contents of fertilized egg has already been stated, but in the blastula the same can be traced in parts on the ventral wall of the blastula. The bulk of the ventral half of the blastula is made up of columnar cells forming the ectodermal area while the endodermal area is formed by the larger yolky cells. Just anterior to the endodermal plate between it and the ectodermal region, is a small area of smaller cells which are chorda cells. From these chorda cells notochord is developed. The cells forming *neural plate* lying infront of chorda cells. The mesodermal crescent consists of small cells bounding the endodermal plate on its lateral and posterior borders.

From this account we can conclude that the animal pole and vegetal pole are the future ectoderm and endoderm respectively. In between is a girdling zone which is subdivided into prospective *mesoderm, notochord* and *neural plate*.

Gastrulation

Gastrulation is a process in which the presumptive or prospective areas of the ovum move to take their final positions in the embryo. The external lining consists of presumptive epidermis and nervous system. The internal lining consists mainly of the presumptive gut material. The presumptive material of the notochord and the mesodermal crescent lie on the rim of the cup. During gastrulation presumptive gut material, notochord and mesoderm disappear from the surface of the embryo into the anterior where they belong. Only ectodermal cells are persisted on the outer surface.

The entire process of gastrulation can be studied under following heads:

Invagination

Gastrulation is initiated when the blastoderm at the vegetal pole becomes flat and subsequently bends inward, so that the whole embryo, instead of being spherical, becomes converted into a cup shaped structure. During invagination, the invaginated layer of endodermal cells gradually eliminates the entire blastocoel and comes to lie against the micromeres. Towards the peripheral region small blastocoel persists for a short time. At

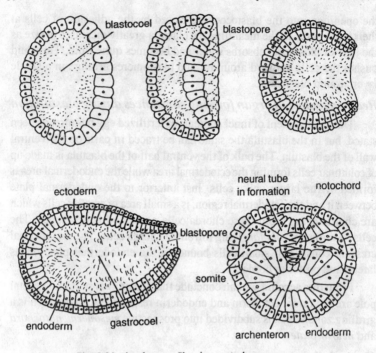

Fig. 3.31. *Amphioxus*. Showing gastrular processes.

this stage one can apply the term gastrula to the cup like structure consisting an outer layer of cells, the ectoderm, and an inner layer mesoderm, since this layer also contains the future mesoderm. The cavity enclosed by mesentodermal layer, is the *archenteron* or *gastrocoel*, the communication of archenteron to the out side can be labelled as *blastopore*.

Involution

It has been observed, however, that there is also a rapid proliferation of cells at the rim of the blastopore and is referred to as involution. This inturn is made possible by active cell division. These proliferated cells arrange themselves to form six transverse rows of cells just anterior to the dorsal blastoporal lip. As the involution proceeds the cells of three rows are turned over the edge of the lip and into the growing archenteron roof and thus become a part of the hypoblast as well as a source of the notochord, while remaining three transverse rows of cells remain out side as part of the dorsal epiblast and furnish material for the neural tube.

Epiboly

The occurrence of epiboly in *Amphioxus* is doubtful but some embryologists are of the opinion that still other factors are at work in gastrulation, as for example, epiboly.

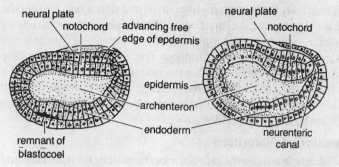

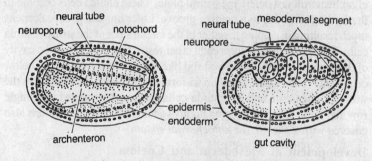

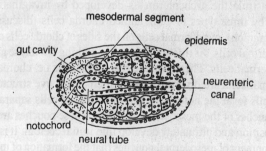

Fig. 3.32. Showing post gastrular processes.

POST GASTRULAR DEVELOPMENT

Formation of the Neural Tube

With the completion of gastrulation, a strip of ectodermal cells in the region of midgut dorsal line enlarges to form the neural plate, which flattens and sinks inwards. The ectoderm on the sides of neural plate now rises up to form the *neural folds* which are gradually extended round the lateral lips of blastopore. Then these folds start growing to meet each other over the neural plate, beginning at the posterior end.

These folds finally meet together in the mid-dorsal line. On the other hand, at the same time, the lateral edges of neural plate have grown towards each other, resulting in the formation of the *neural tube*. As the neural folds meet together over the blastopore, they form a roof over the latter and it is obvious at this stage, that the neural tube is in communication with the hinder end of archenteron through a short *neurenteric canal*. The neurenteric canal is then interrupted by the closure of blastopore which has been a minute orifice.

Formation of Notochord

The chorda cells, in the gastrula, are present along the mid-dorsal wall of archenteron just below the neural plate. These chorda cells become in the form of strip due to a median groove. Later on, this groove deepens much resulting in coming together of the lateral sides of the strip of chorda cells. These sides finally meet each other restricting completely the cavity of the groove. In this way a solid rod like notochord is formed just below central nervous system. Later on so-formed notochord is cut off from the wall of archenteron and the chorda-cells become re-arranged in a single row and these cells also become highly vacuolated. The notochord is also covered with a sheath, the *notochordal sheath*.

Development of Mesoderm and Coelom

In gastrula the archenteron, is developed by invagination and is bounded by three types of cells named chorda cells (discussed in the above paragraph), mesodermal cells on the sides of chorda cells and mainly by endodermal cells. As this archenteron is nothing but future gut, is lined by endodermal cells. Therefore, the rest of the cells i.e. chorda cells and mesodermal cells are diverted to form their respective structures. Thus chorda cells form the notochord and mesodermal cells separate to form paired pouches or the mesodermal pouches. These pouches are in dorso-lateral position and ultimately develop into initial coelom. It is only after the development of mesodermal pouches that the formation of mesodermal coelom starts. These pouches are paired and develop segmentally forming lateral coelomic pouches. Each pouch is later on disconnected from archenteron and thus encloses a cavity. The remaining cavity with the archenteron becomes the cavity of the gut and persists as alimentary canal in the adult animal. The ventral end of each pair of pouches arrange themselves in the midventral line. Later on their partition in the mid ventral line disappears forming a continued coelom of the same pair.

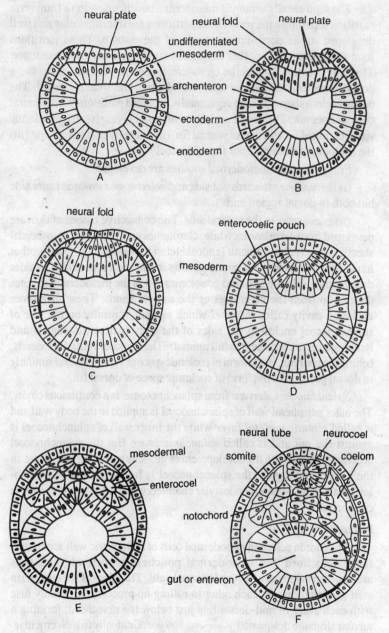

Fig. 3.33. Showing the formation of coelom, notochord and neural tube.

The segmentally arranged mesodermal pouches develop a transverse partition separating the two. These partitions are intermuscular and well developed in the dorso-lateral region of the embryo. These partitions soon disappears and another horizontal partition comes into existence. This new partition divides the mesodermal coelom into two spaces viz. a dorsal space called *myocoel* and ventral space the *splanchnocoel*. The dorsal coelom shows definite segmentally arranged partitions while ventral coelom does not. The dorsal coelom or myocoel gives rise to (i) coelomic space of dorsal fin and that of ventral fin, (ii) lateral lymph spaces and (iii) the coelom of sclerotomes or the sclerocoel.

From the dorsal mesodermal somites are developed:

(i) *dermatomes* towards out side and *sclerotomes* towards inner side but both in dorsal region and

(ii) *gonotomes* in the ventral side. The connective tissues of skin are developed from dermatomes while sclerotomes give rise to the notochordal sheath and nerve cord sheath (endoskeleton in vertebrates). On the other hand, the gonotomes give rise to gonads in the ventral position. Besides dermatomes, sclerotomes, and gonotomes rest of the mesodermal somites develop to from the myotomes or the muscle bands. These myotomes enclose a cavity called *myocoel* which extends ventrally on the side of splanchnocoel enclosing the sides of the body (where the gonads and lymph spaces are located in adult animal). The myocoel ventrally extends, behind the pharynx, in the form of coelomic space of ventral fin and similarly in dorsal position in the form of coelomic space of dorsal fin.

Splanchnocoel, derived from splanchnotome, is a continuous cavity. The outer peripheral wall of splanchnocoel is applied to the body wall and is called *somatic parietal layer* while the inner wall of splanchnocoel is against the gut and is called *splanchnic layer.* But the splanchnocoel becomes reduced with the development of gill-slits and an atrium. Thus, in the pharyngeal region, the splanchnocoel is in the form of two dorso-lateral and a mid-ventral endostylar channels with their paired transverse connections.

Formation of Gut

The chorda cells and mesodermal cells of archenteric wall separate to form notochord and mesodermal pouches respectively and thus archenteron is left only with endodermal cells. The edges of the endoderm start growing towards each other (a rolling up process) and finally fuse with each other in mid-dorsal line just below the notochord, forming a tubular structure designated as *mesenteron gut.* Gradually two diverticulae. one right and one left are developed from the dorsal side of the anterior part of archenteron. The right diverticulum gets separated from gut and enlarges, to form the cavity of the head while left diverticulum acquires (no doubt after separated from gut) an opening into the oral hood on the left side of the larva forming the *Hatschek's pit*.

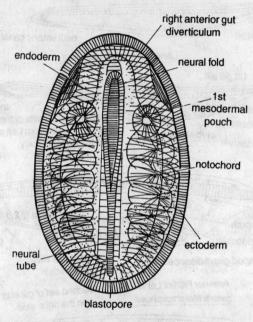

Fig. 3.34. V.S. of larva.

Hatching

The embryo before hatching has developed eight pairs of somites and the outer cells become ciliated. By the completion of gastrulation the embryo gets dettached from the egg membrane and moves freely with the help of cilia in the surface layer of sea. The larva is incapable of feeding as mouth and anus are not yet formed and therefore it is called as *gastrula larva*.

Larval Development

After the eight mesodermal somites have been formed, the embryo develops cilia all over the body and hatches out as the gastrula larva which swims about the surface of the water with the help of cilia. The larval stage in *Amphioxus* persists for about 3 to 4 months. In the early stage of larva when it had just started swimming there is no formation of mouth and anus. It is therefore, incapable of feeding. Just after hatching.

on the anterior side of the dorsal part, a *gut diverticulum* is given out. This diverticulum in the beginning is a single large pouch which then splits off

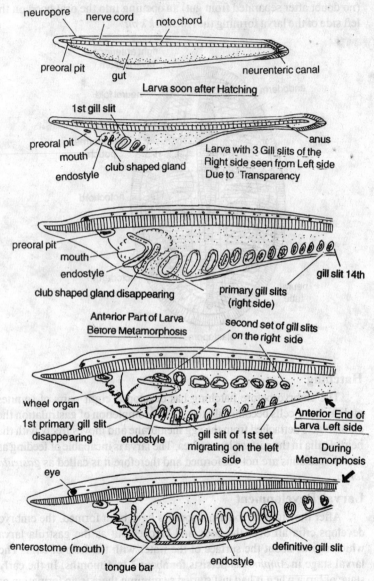

Fig. 3.35. Larva before and after metamorphosis.

into two pouches namely *left gut diverticulum* and *right gut diverticulum*. These two pouches then loose their connections from the cavity of the gut and the right pouch extends anteriorly becomes larger in size and forms the cavity of the head, while the left diverticulum remains smaller and develops an opening on the ventral side of the head forming the *Hatschek's plate.*

The formation of *mouth* and *anus* begin as an invagination of ectoderm on the ventral side towards the left at the two extremities of the gut. The invaginations of ectoderm meet with a pouch like evagination of the endoderm of the gut at the two ends on the left ventral side. The two invaginations and pouch like evagination meet with each other and their partitions disappear marking the opening of mouth and anus. The formation of *mouth* and *anus* thus permits the larva to feed upon small planktons.

The first cleft is developed as a diverticulum of anterior end of pharynx on left side of the larva but instead of developing into a regular slit, it forms a coiled glandular tube-like structure the, *club shaped gland*. This gland which is of unknown functions, opens out ventrally to the mouth. This gland marks the beginning of the gill clefts in the larva and disappears during metamorphosis.

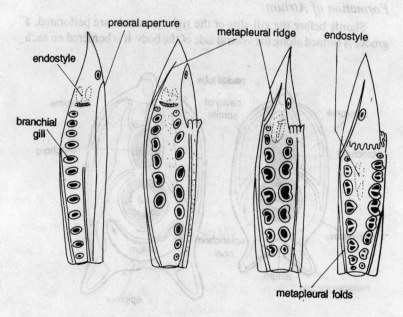

Fig. 3.36. Formation and arrangement of gills and metapleural folds.

Fourteen gill-clefts are simultaneously formed on the left side of the midventral line of the gut. But soon these fourteen gill-clefts shift towards the right side of the mid ventral line and retain their openings into the gut. After they have shifted towards the right side, a set of eight more gill clefts are developed on the right side but lying dorsally to the first set of fourteen gill-clefts. Both the sets of gill-clefts form two rows on the right side of the gut (pharynx) and none on the left. Out of first set of fourteen gill-clefts, six posterior clefts disappear leaving behind eight clefts. At this stage both the rows of the gill-clefts are having the same number of gill-clefts which is eight. The remaining eight gill cleft side of first set now shift back to left side in such a way that these eight lie just opposite to the other eight of the right side. These gill clefts are supported by the primary gill bars. Then both the sets of gill-clefts (eight each) shift towards the laternal wall of the pharynx. In the meantime secondary gill bars are developed. Further gill clefts are added posterior to these in pairs uptill about 19 pairs have been formed in the lateral wall of the pharynx.

The endostyle also develops first as a groove on the left ventral side of pharynx and during shifting of clefts occupies the mid ventral line forming a ciliated median groove.

Formation of Atrium

Shortly before the gill-slits of the right hand side are perforated, a groove is formed along the ventral side of the body. It is bordered on each

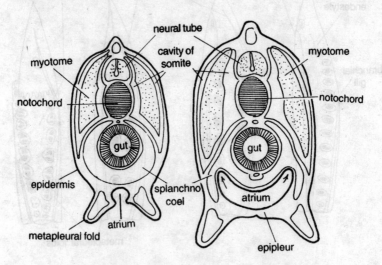

Fig. 3.37. Showing the formation of atrium.

side by a fold of body wall-the *right* and *left metapleural folds*. These folds internally enclose a part of coelom around the pharynx. The formation of atrium starts just after the formation of metapleural folds. During the formation of atrium, a diverticulum in the mid ventral line develops into the body cavity through an invagination of the ectoderm. This invagination marks the beginning of the atrium. This atrium then develops further to occupy the entire space around the gut in the region of the pharynx. The gill-clefts which were opening into the coelom now opens through small aperture into atrium. The opening at the point of invagination of ectoderm closes anteriorly but remains open at its hinder end as the atriopore. The cavity of the atrium covers the entire body coelom as in pharyngeal region.

Metamorphosis

During metamorphosis the free swimming larva, after passing three months free swimming pelagic life, settles down to the sea bottom. As a result of metamorphosis the asymmetrical larva becomes a bilateral symmetrical adult and at the same time the feeding nature is also affected. Larva is planktonic feeder which, after metamorphosis changes to ciliary feeder. Many other conspicuous changes take place during metamorphosis. The mouth shifts to the midventral line and the anus shifts toward the anterior side so that tail becomes distinct. The club-shaped gland becomes indistinct and disappears. Nephridia, which are excretory organs, are developed at the dorsal end of the gill-clefts. Oral hood, velum, oral cirri and gonads are also developed. After metamorphosis, the larva changes into bottom living adult and take up usual burrowing habit.

AFFINITIES OF *AMPHIOXUS*

Amphioxus possesses chordate as well as many primitive characters.

Affinities with non-chordates

1. Development of coelom is enterocoelic in both.
2. The heart is absent.
3. Presence of segmentally arranged nephridia as present in polychaete annelids.
4. Gastrulation occurs by invagination.

Affinities with Urochordata

Amphioxus shows following similarities with urochordates :

1. In presence of endostyle.
2. In the perforation of pharyngeal wall by numerous gill-slits which open into atrial cavity.

3. In ciliary mode of feeding.

4. In the presence of atrium around the pharynx.

5. Development of notochord and nerve cord are similar in both.

However, *Amphioxus*, differs from urochordates in following characters:

1. Urochordates are sedentary but *Amphioxus* is free swimming.

2. Test is present in urochordates but absent in *Amphioxus*.

3. Alimentary canal is straight in *Amphioxus* but 'U' shaped in urochordates.

4. Nephridia present in *Amphioxus* but absent in urochordates.

5. The heart is absent in *Amphioxus* but present in urochordates.

6. Gonoducts are absent in *Amphioxus* but present in urochordates.

7. *Amphioxus* is unisexual but ascidians are bisexual and asexual reproduction is also reported in them.

Affinities with Chordata
Similarities

1. Body wall is differentiated into epidermis and dermis.

2. Mouth is ventrally situated.

3. Coelom is similar to that of chordates.

4. Notochord is situated on the dorsal side beneath the nerve cord.

5. Presence of midgut diverticulum that can be compared with the liver.

6. Pharyngeal gill-slits are present.

7. Dorsal tubular nerve cord is present.

8. Myotomes are present.

9. Development is similar to that of chordates.

10. Presence of hepatic portal system.

However, it differs from higher chordates in following respects:

1. Absence of head, brain and cranium.

2. Presence of single layered epidermis.

3. Ciliary mode of feeding.

4. Heart is absent.

5. Presence of atrium around the pharynx.

6. Presence of colourless blood without respiratory pigment.

7. Absence of special sense organs like eyes, ears and other sense organs.

8. Absence of kidneys.

On the basis of above discussion it can be concluded that *Amphioxus* seems to be a simplified or degenerate chordate. The specialized characters are secondary adaptations based on the peculiar mode of life. *Amphioxus* is definitely a chordate but it can not be placed with urochordates or fishes. Therefore, it is placed near the urochordates as a sub-phylum - Cephalochordata.

Revision Questions

1. Describe the habits, habitat and external morphology of *Branchiostoma*.

2. Describe the alimentary canal and mode of feeding in *Branchiostoma*.

3. Describe the circulatory system of *Amphioxus*.

4. Give a comparative account of digestive system of *Balanoglossus, Herdmania* and *Amphioxus*.

5. Describe the excretory system of *Amphioxus* and compare it with that of *Herdmania*.

6. Describe the affinities of *Amphioxus*.

7. Give an account of development of *Branchiostoma*.

8. Describe the development of *Amphioxus* upto the formation of three germ layers.

9. Give an account of development of coelom and mesoderm in *Branchiostoma*.

10. Draw neat and well labelled diagrams of *Amphioxus* (a) T.S. passing through pharynx, (b) T.S. passing through intestine. (No description is required).

11. Write short notes on : (a) Oral hood, (b) Velum, (c) Nephridium, (d) Cephalic eye-spot, (e) Endostyle.

General comparison in *Balanoglossus*, *Herdmania* and *Branchiostoma*.

Characters	*Balanoglossus*	*Herdmania*	*Branchiostoma*
1. Distribution	Marine, world-wide in distribution	Marine, world-wide in distribution.	Marine and world-wide in distribution.
2. Habits & habitat	Solitary and tubicolous animal.	Solitary and fixed animal.	Solitary, burrowing and free-swimming animal.
3. Shape	Elongated, cylindrical, worm-like animal.	Degenerate, bag-like animal.	Fish-like, laterally compressed animal.
4. Division of body	Body in divisible into proboscis, collar and trunk.	Unsegmented without head and tail.	Segmented without distinct head.
5. Post-anal tail	Absent	Absent	Present.
6. Fins	Absent	Absent	Median dorsal, ventral and caudal fins are present
7. Test	Absent	A thick, soft and translucent test, made up of tunicine, is present.	Absent
8. Coelom	Coelom is enterocoelous, divisible into protocoel, mesocoel and metacoel.	True coelom is absent replaced by atrial cavity.	True coelom is present but reduced by atrial cavity.

Characters	Balanoglossus	Herdmania	Branchiostoma
9. Atrial cavity	Absent	Highly developed	Well developed.
10. Notochord	True notochord is absent, however, stomocord is present in proboscis.	Notochord is present in tail of larva, absent in adult.	A mid-dorsal, rod-like notochord present throughout the life.
11. Muscles	Unsegmented animal	Unsegmented animal	Metamenically segmented. Muscles in the form of myotomes.
12. Oral-hood	Absent	Absent	Present, formed by the dorsal and lateral projection of the anterior end of trunk.
13. Alimentary canal	Complete, straight tube-like structure.	Complete, coiled.	Complete straight.
14. Pharynx	Large, simple with two dorsal linear rows of gill-slits.	Large, complex, with two or several pairs of lateral gill-slits.	Same as that of *Herdmania.*
15. Feeding mechanism	Ciliary or filter feeders.	Ciliary feeder	Ciliary feeder.
16. Respiratory organs	Respiratory organs are absent.	Same as that of *Blanoglossus.* Respiration	Same as that of *Balanoglossus.*

Characters	Balanoglossus	Herdmania	Branchiostoma
		through general body surface.	
17. Heart.	A dorsal heart or central sinus is present situated in the proboscis.	Heart is present enclosed in pericardium.	Heart is absent.
18. Excretory organs.	Glomerulus is present in proboscis.	Neural glands, pyloric gland and nephrocytes are excretory organs.	Protonephridia are excretory organs.
19. Nervous system.	Intra-epidermal.	Simple and degenerate. It includes long, solid nerve ganglion	Much simplified consists of nerve cord, nerves and autonomic nervous system.
20. Sexes	Unisexual	Bisexual	Unisexual.
21. Gonads	One to several pairs	One pair	Several pairs metamerically arranged.
22. Gonoducts	Absent	Present	Absent.
23. Development.	Direct or indirect. If indirect through tornaria larva.	Indirect through tadpole larva	Indirect through a larval stage called gastrula larva.

Comparison of alimentary canals and associated glands in *Balanoglossus*, *Herdmania* and *Branchiostoma*.

	Characters	Balanoglossus	Herdmania	Branchiostoma
1.	Alimentary canal	Complete, straight tube-like narrow canal from mouth to anus.	Complete, curved narrow tuble with intestinal and rectal loops.	Complete, straight tube from mouth to anus.
2.	Mouth	Wide, circular aperture usually remains open, situated mid-ventrally between proboscis and collar.	Mouth or branchial aperture is four-sided and guarded by four lips, situated on branchial siphon.	Location of mouth is controversial. By homology with vertebrates, the anterior opening of oral-hood is regarded as a mouth. *Enterostome* in velum is also considered to be the mouth.
3.	Buccal cavity	Short without tentacles. Velum is absent.	It is a cavity of branchial siphon with a circlet of branchial tentacles which acts as sieve. Below the tentacles is peribranchial zone having dorsal tubercle. At the upper end of pharynx there are two thin ciliated	It is a spacious vestibula of oral hood. The lateral margins of oral-hood are provided with 10-11 pairs of oral cirri. Velum is present, which is provided with valar tentacles having sensory papillae.

Characters	Balanoglossus	Herdmania	Branchiostoma
		peripharyngeal bands. Velum is absent.	
4. Pharynx	It is divided into a dorsal branchial chamber and a ventral chamber or digestive part by lateral parabranchial ridges. The branchial chamber bears gill-slits.	Pharynx or branchial sac is perforated by gill-slits.	Pharynx is divides into a small anterio-dorsal prebranchial region and a larger posterior branchial region by lateral oblique ciliated peripharyngeal bands.
5. Endostyle	It is absent.	Extends mid-ventrally along floor of pharynx	It is shallow groove situated mid-ventrally along the floor of pharynx.
6. Hyperpharyngeal groove.	It is absent	Dorsal lamina present with tongue-like processes called *languets*.	It is a ciliated groove. The languets are absent.
7. Gill-slits.	Dorso-lateral U-shaped gill-slits open into branchial sacs which open externally though gill-pores.	About 2,00,000 gill-slits open into atrial cavity.	Only 150-200 pairs of gill-slits are present that open into atrial cavity.
8. Oesophagus	A small oesophagus is present.	Branchial sac opens into the oesophagus, which is	It is short tube like. At the junction of oesophagus and

Characters	Balanoglossus	Herdmania	Branchiostoma
		guarded by two large flaps. Oesophagus is thick walled short tube; oesophageal diverticulum is absent.	midgut there is an oesophageal diverticulum.
9. Stomach	It is not demarcated clearly from the intestine.	Well demarcated and sphinctered at both the ends.	It is not demarcated from the intestine.
10. Intestine	It is a straight tube. Anterior or hepatic region is sacculated forming hepatic caeca.	It is a 'U' shaped tube enclosing the left gonad. The iliocolic ring is absent.	It is a straight tube, internally lined by cilia containing lateral ciliary tract and iliocolic ring.
11. Rectum.	It is not differentiated.	Well differentiated and internally lined with cilia.	Well demarcated and heavily ciliated.
12. Anus	The intestine opens out through anus situated at the tip of trunk. Anal spincter is present.	Rectum curves dorsally to open into cloaca by anus bordered by four lips.	Rectum opens out by anus. It is a small, cicular sphinctered aperture lying at the base of caudal fin.
13. Digestive glands	Definite glands are unknown.	Liver is bilobed. A branching pyloric gland is present in the wall of stomach and intestine. The pyloric gland is	A midgut diverticulum is present which functions as liver. Pyloric gland is absent.

Characters	Balanoglossus	Herdmania	Branchiostoma
14. Atrial cavity	It is absent	supposed to be digestive as well as excretory. It is present. The gill-slits and anus open here. The atrial cavity opens out through atrial aperture guarded by four lips and situated on atrial siphon.	It is present and only the gill-slits open in it. The atrial cavity opens outside through atriopore.

Comparison of pharynx in *Balanoglossus, Herdmania* and *Branchiostoma*

Characters	Balanoglossus	Herdmania	Branchiostoma
1. Location	It is present in the anterior 1/3 part of trunk. This is known as branchiogenital region.	Occupies the major part of the body cavity.	It occupies about 1/2 anterior part of the body.
2. Shape and division	Elongated, divided into two parts by lateral parabranchial ridges. Dorsal branchial chamber and ventral is digestive part.	It is large sac-like structure. Differentiated into anterior prebranchial zone and a much larger posterior branchial sac. Both are separated by ciliated peripharyngeal bands.	It is a large, cylindrical and laterally compressed chamber. It is also divided into a small anterior prebranchial zone and the pharynx proper by ciliated peripharyngeal bands.

Characters	Balanoglossus	Herdmania	Branchiostoma
3. Attachment	It remains attached with the body-wall by dorsal and ventral mesenteries.	Attached mid-ventrally to mantle.	Attached dorsally to body wall.
4. Atrium.	It is absent	Atrium or peribranchial cavity surrounds the pharynx on all the sides except the ventral. Atrium opens out through the atripore.	Atrium surrounds pharynx on all the sides except dorsal It opens through atripore.
5. Relationship between mouth and pharynx	Mouth opens into a short-buccal cavity which leads into pharynx.	Small four lipped mouth is situated at the branchial siphon. It opens into pharynx through buccal cavity.	Large oval mouth, bordered by oral hood with buccal cirri and guarded by velar tentacles opens into pharynx through a circular aperture called enterostome.
6. Pharyngeal cavity.	It is simple and uniformly lined by cilia and mucous goblet cells.	Internal wall is complicated and longitudinally folded with cilia and glands restricted into definite tracts.	Pharyngeal cavity is very much complicated with definite ciliary and glandular tracts.
7. Gill-slits.	The branchial parts of pharynx bears many 'U'	Pharynx is perforated by about 2,00,000 elongated	Lateral walls of pharynx are perforated by 150-200 pairs

Characters	Balanoglossus	Herdmania	Branchiostoma
	shaped gill-slits which open into branchial sacs. The branchial sacs open out through gill-pores. In *Balanoglossus misakiensis*, first four branchial sacs join so as to form a common branchial sac opening by a single gill-pore. Gill-bars have many long, vibratile cilia.	gill-slits. The slits leading into atrial cavity. The gill-slits are present on all the sides except mantle.	of vertically oblique narrow gill-slits. Gill-slits are of two types- primary and secondary. Each gill-slits opens directly into the atrium.
8. Hyperpharyngeal tract.	It is absent.	A ciliated hyperpharyngel band or dorsal lamina hangs mid-dorsally from which hangs curved bodies called languets.	A median groove is known as epipharyngeal or hyperpharyngeal groove is found opposite to the endostyle. It is ciliated and without languets.
9. Hypopharyngeal tact or Endostyle.	It is absent	A highly developed endostyle is present midventrally on the floor of pharynx. It consists of five ciliary tracts altern-	An endostyle similar to that of *Herdmania* is present.

Characters	Balanoglossus	Herdmania	Branchiostoma
10. Peripharyngeal bands.	Absent	ating with four glandular tracts. Dorsal lamina and endostyle are connected by the peripharyngeal ciliated bands.	Epipharyngeal groove and endostyle are connected anteriorly by a pair of lateral peripharyngeal ciliated bands.
11. Relationship between pharynx and intestine.	Pharynx directly opens into intestine.	Pharynx is communicated with intestine through oesophagus and stomach	Pharynx opens into intestine via a short oesophagus and midgut.

Comparison of Excretory System in *Balanoglossus*, *Herdmania* and *Branchiostoma*.

Characters	Balanoglossus	Herdmania	Branchiostoma
1. Excretory organs	Glomerulus is the excretory organ projecting into proboscis coelom.	Excretory organ is the neural gland present mid-dorsally embedded in mantle, above the nerve ganglion.	90-100 pairs of protonephridia present segmentally one above each gill-slit.
2. Structure	Glomerulus is made up of several blind tubules formed by peritoneum	Neural gland consists of peripheral and central tubules leading into a small	Each nephridium consists of lower ventral limb, terminating blindly. The upper

Characters	Balanoglossus	Herdmania	Branchiostoma
	covering buccal diverticulum, heart and central sinus. Projections containing blood vessels.	duct. The duct opens at the base of dorsal tubercle by a large ciliated funnel.	horizontal limb opening by a nephridiopore into atrium.
3. Solenocytes	Solenocytes are absent.	Solenocytes are absent.	Several branches are given out by both the limbs. Each receiving a tuft of solenocytes or flame cells.
4. Physiology of excretion	Excretory products from blood are extracted by the peritoneal cells of glomerulus and than discharge into proboscis coelom and finally to out side through proboscis pore.	Nephrocytes collect waste products and discharge through aperture of the neural gland into prebranchial zone of pharynx.	Nitrogenous waste products diffuse from surrounding blood and coelomic fluid into solenocytes discharge into atrium through nephridiopores. The waste products are passed out through atriopore with out going water current.
5. Hatschek's nephridium	Absent	Absent	It lies in the roof of oral-hood. Its structure and function are similar to those of a protonephridium.
6. Brown funel	Absent	Absent	A pair of sac-like brown funels are situated dorsally

Characters	Balanoglossus	Herdmania	Branchiostoma
7. Renal papillae	Absent	Absent	upon pharynx are considered to be excretory. Groups of renal papillae present on atrial floor are also considered to be excretory in function.
8. Hormones secretion	Unknown	Neural gland secretes a hormone controlling oviposition, development and metamorphosis. It is considered to be homologous to pituitary glands of vertebrates.	Unknown.

Comparison of nervous system in *Balanoglossus*, *Herdmania* and *Branchiostoma*.

Characters	Balanoglossus	Herdmania	Branchiostoma
1. Grade	Grade of nervous system is primitive. It resembles that of coelenterates or echinoderms.	Adult nervous system is poorly developed.	Nervous system is better developed.
2. Structure	It consists of a subepidermal plexus of nerve	There is a single solid, elongated ganglion lying	Nervous system consists of a hollow tube or dorsal

Characters	Balanoglossus	Herdmania	Branchiostoma
	cells and fibres, forming two definit nerve cords dorsal and ventral. Dorsal nerve cord is hollow.	between the branchial and atrial siphons	nerve cord lying above the notochord.
3. Brain	Brain is absent	Nerve ganglion is also known as brain or cerebral ganglion.	Anterior end of nerve cord dilates forming the brain or cerebral vesicle.
4. Nerves	Definit nerves are absent	Brain sends three nerves to branchial siphon and two nerves to atrial siphon; spinal nerves are absent.	At the anterior end there are two pairs of sensory nerves to oral-hood, cirri and sense organs. Behind the cerebral vesicle, spinal nerves arise from nerve cord. Spinal nerve has a dorsal root with afferent sensory fibres and a ventral root made up of motor or efferent fibres. On dorsal side the nerve cord has some giant cells and giant fibres situated along its length.
5. Autonomic nerves system	Absent	Absent	Present.

4

Salpa

Salpa belongs to Sub-phylum Urochordata. Urochordates constitute a highly successful side line of chordate evolution.

Here detail anatomy and life history of *Salpa* has been described as a representative of the class *Thaliacea* considering the characteristic features which are of special significance among the members of series.

Systematic position of *Salpa*

Salpa is a member of order Salpida sub-order Hemimyria which comes under class *Thaliacea* and subphylum *Urochordata*. Salpians are free swimming pelagic forms which exhibit alternation of generation in their life history. During sexual phase they form colonies. About 15 species of *Salpa* are pelagic and found in the oceans. During life history of each species of *Salpa* occur two phases:

(i) The asexual phase which is solitary and known as *Proles solitaria*.

(ii) Aggregated sexual form known as *Proles gregaria*.

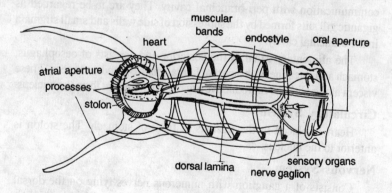

Fig. 4.1. Showing structure of *Salpa*.

139

Structure

Salpians are transparent, pelagic animals and opaque at the heart and digestive glands. The body is enclosed in soft gelatinous test. The body is elongated dorso-ventrally and having oral aperture at anterior end and atrial aperture at posterior end which is slightly dorsal. Both these apertures lead into large cavities, *peribranchial* and *atrial cavities* respectively. These two cavities are in free communication at the side of obliquely running dorsal lamina. Muscular bands are placed dorsally and laterally and do not encircle the body in most cases i.e. they do not meet on ventral side. The anterior portion of dorsal lamina in some cases prolonged to form a prominent tentacular organ, the dorsal tactile projecting into branchial sac.

Digestive System

Pharynx is without any side wall stigmata, and freely communicates with atrial cavity. On each side, *endostyle* is present in usual form, and the dorsomedian wall of pharynx is represented by the so called gills which take an oblique position across the body from near the ganglion to the opening of oesophagus where it terminates. The *oesophagus* leads into a gut, which possesses a *stomach*. The *pyloric gland* is twisted on itself and constitutes the *nucleus*. The *anus* opens into atrial cavity in the posterior region.

The large spaces at the side of dorsal lamina, often called as *gill* or *branchial sacs*, by means of which the cavity of branchial sac is placed in communication with peri-branchial cavity. They are to be regarded as gigantic gill slits formed by the supression of side walls and small stigmata in the branchial cavity.

The alimentary canal at the posterior end consists of oesophagus, stomach and intestine with a part of lateral gastric gland and caeca. These viscera along with the reproductive organs when present form the nucleus.

Circulatory System

Heart is placed in the nucleus in front of stomach. The stolon is anterior to the nucleus.

Nervous System

Consists of a ganglion with numerous nerves lying on the dorsal side. It has a horse-shoe shaped brownish pigmented band which is regarded as eye.

Dorsal Tubercle

The dorsal tubercle of ciliated pit is a short diverticulum of pharynx the epipharyngeal band. It is without a glandular part and does not extend as far as back as the ganglion. On the ventral side of ganglion there are two glands (sub-neural glands) which open separately into pharynx just in front of the peripharyngeal band. *Otocysts* are absent. *Metcaff* compared glandular organ with otocyst. These organs remained as lateral neural glands. They do not open into dorsal tubercle but separately into the pharynx. These have also been regarded as nephridia.

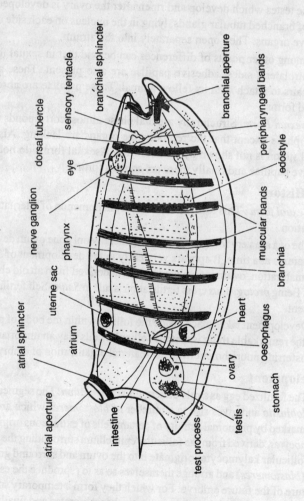

Fig. 4.2. *Salpa*. Showing sexual and asexual phases.

Reproductive System

The sexual form often called as *chain form* (*Proles gregaria*) or *blastozooid*. It differs from asexual form :

(i) In having reproductive organs; and (ii) Absence of stolon.

Ovary in young form is placed in the nucleus, by the right side of the intestine, and is connected with the epithelium of the atrial cavity by a stalk.

The testes which develop and ripen after the ovary is developed, are a pair of branched tubular glands, lying in the nucleus on each side of the digestive organs. They open separately into the atrium.

Among other points of differences can be said that in sexual forms, on ventrolateral sides, adhesive papillae are also present. These are in eight pairs to attach with its fellow animal. These papillae are absent in isolated forms.

Asexual Form. Structurally asexual phase almost corresponds to the sexual phase except that the reproductive organs are lacking. Also the ventral stolon is not shown by sexual forms. Asexual forms do not have adhesive papillae and finally these are solitary forms.

Life History

Sexual form : This form shows a great phenomenon of alternation of generation.

The ova are very few in number and generally only one ovum develops and matures at a time. It appears very early in the development of *Salpa*. After maturation, ovum is fertilized by sperm derived from an old chain of *Salpa*. Being *protogynous* cross fertilization is rule in *Salpa*. Self fertilization is absent.

Development takes place inside the follicle within the body of parent. Here the remarkable thing is that the follicular cells play an important role in transferring nourishment from the material organization of embryo.

Development

The fertilized egg as a rule undergoes *segmentation*. The segmentation is *holoblastic* and gives rise to a number of *blastomeres* which are for a time marked by phenomal activity of certain cells of extraneous origin. The *kalymocytes*, derived from the follicular epithellium surrounding the ovum. The follicular kalymocytes originate into the ovum and surround group of cells (*blastomeres*) and arrange themselves so as to reproduce the essential structure of the future embryo. For which they form a temporary support. After some time blastomeres become actively proliferated and finally press upon and absorb by their kalymocytes and so eventually taken up their proper place in building up the organs. Some regard kalymocytes as mere nutritive.

At an early period of development a part of the surface of embryo, on its ventral edge, becomes separated off along with a part of wall of cavity and oviduct (oviduct - diverticulum from atrium) in which it lies to form the placenta in which the embryonic and maternal blood streams circulating in

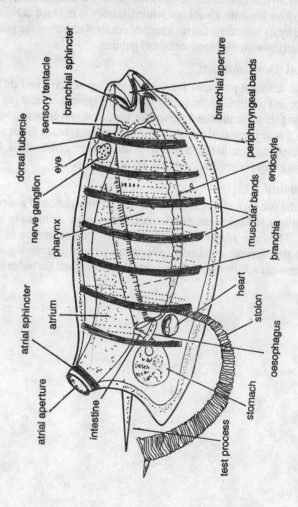

Fig. 4.3. *Salpa*. An oozooid.

close proximity and so allow the convergence of nutrients to the developing embryo by means of large migrating placental cells.

As seen in the later stage number of cells placed at posterior end of the body along side the future nucleus become filled up with oil globules to form "*cloaoblast*" which are used up in later development as food.

The development is direct and it may be said that this young asexual *Salpa* (solitary) differs from the corresponding form in the life cycle of *Doliolum*, in that its tail is no longer a locomotary organ but is represented by a nutritive mass the cloaoblast while the body is in place of being free attached by its ventral surface to a special organ of nutrition-the placenta-in connection with the blood stream of parents.

Asexual Development

This sexually produced larva becomes free solitary and differs in structure and habits from the parent and has no reproductive organ. After swimming for some time, it develops the ventral stolon on which buds are formed. These are sexual salpas. These are let free solitary forms and are still connecting together for a time as chain of aggregated salpas. Before separating they become the adult sexual individuals.

Conclusion

In the life history of the *Salpa* we find an alternation of generation. Both solitary and aggregated (colonials) forms being included in one life history. The term *phroditism* is modified by the occurrence of a very marked protogynous condition i.e. ova mature earlier than the sperms which prevent self fertilization and puts the individuals for out-breeding.

5

Doliolum

Doliolum is free swimming pelagic and cosmopolitan in distribution being recorded from both cold and warm oceans of the world. It is an interesting example of tunicate, since it exhibits an *alternation of generation* between the two morphologically distinct (dimorphic) phases in its life history. The two phases are asexually reproducing *solitary phase*; and a sexually reproducing *gregarine phase*.

Structure

The solitary phase in represented by a solitary gonozooid which is about one to two centimeters long. It is typically barrel shaped with branchial and atrial apertures situated at the opposite ends. The branchial as well as atrial apertures are fringed with 10-12 small lobes provided with sense organs. The gelatinous test is thin, tough, transparent and contains no cilia. The body wall contains 8 or 9 annular muscular bands, which completely encircle the body like the loop. The Ist and last of these muscular bands serve as terminal sphincter muscles for their respective orifices.

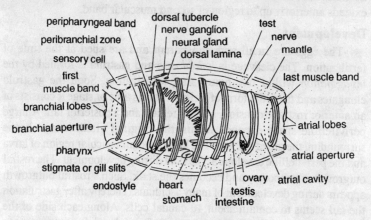

Fig. 5.1. Structure of *Doliolum*.

145

The tentacles are absent. The pharynx is large occupying at least the posterior peribranchial or atrial cavity upto the posterior end. The postero-lateral walls of the pharynx are pierced by a large number of small stigmata. Thus there is a free straight passage for water, along the long axis of the body from branchial to atrial aperture through the pharynx, stigmata and atrial cavity. The animal swims about by forcefully rejecting water out through the atrial aperture with the help of annular muscular bands. In a few, however, stigmata occur on the lateral walls of the branchial sacs and in these cases the atrial cavity has corresponding anteriorly directed diverticulae. As usual a ciliated *peripharyngeal band* divides the pharynx into *peribranchial zone* and the *branchial sac proper*. There is a distinct ventral *endostyle* present in the branchial sac, but a dorsal lamina is lacking. The rest of the alimentary canal is wide, a short *oesophagus*, a small subspherical *stomach* and a curved *intestine* lies ventrally and posteriorly to branchial sac. The *heart* is posterior to endostyle in mid-ventral line. The usual neural complex and dorsal tubercle lie at about the middle of dorsal side of the body.

Sexual Reproduction

Doliolum is hermaphrodite. Both the ovary and testes are present on the left of the middle line of the body. The alimentary canal and their ducts open in the atrial cavity. The ovary is pyriform or nearly spherical, while the testis is variable in form in different species. It is short and narrow in *D. mulloni*, while it is elongated and cylindrical or rectangular in *D. varnum*, *D. nationalis*, *D.intermedium* etc. In *D. derticulatum* the elongated testis extends anteriorly up to region of second muscular band.

Development

The eggs are small and transparent and are shed at the time of fertilization. The cleavage is *holoblastic* and gastrula is formed by the *invagination* within five hours after fertilization. Soon the gastrula elongates and takes the form of a cigar. At this time or stage it consists of an anterior rostral extension, a trunk region and a posterior tail. A large perivitelline space expands within the original vitelline membrane surrounding the tailed embryo. The large median vesicular region of larva and the perivitelline envelope act as float during development. The rostral outgrowth is temporary and becomes the stalk. Such a rostral outgrowth appears during development of many ascidians. Thereby after gastrulation the tail seems to contain about 40 caudal cells. Along each side of the notochord about 40 fibrillated muscle cells form a band. It is interesting to note that the structure of notochord and the number of its cells and the cell constituting the muscle bands are just the same as found in most ascidians tadpoles. The tail has no connection with the anterior region where the larval tissues develop and possess no sense organ. Further the tail is not functional. It is retained within perivitelline membrane. It is, therefore, concluded that it is a residual organ indicating a part relationship with ascidians. Thus it is apparent that cleavage, gastrulation and tail formation take place as in other ascidians, but larval sense organs do not develop and larva does not settle down to attach to substratum.

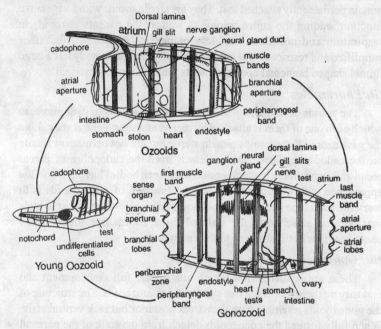

Fig. 5.2. *Doliolum* showing reproductive organs and zooids.

Each tadpole larva metamorphoses without getting fix on a substratum, into a free swimming adult zooid which belongs to the sexually reproducing gregarine phase of *Doliolum*. This zooid is called as an *oozooid* or *nurses* and is characterized by the possession of nine muscular bands, a fewer stigmata confined to posterior wall of branchial sac and an otocyst on the left side of body. Later the oozooid develops in small ventrally placed complex stolon form near its heart and a larger lobe like postero-dorsal out growth called as *cadophore*.

On the ventral stolon, a number of minute projections or buds develop and become constricted from it. Each constricted bud is a little group of cells arranged in seven strings and covered with an ectodermal investment.

By the pseudopodial activity of their ectodermal cells, multiply by division and ultimately reach the cadophore to which become attached, some in lateral rows and some in median rows. Thus giving rise to colony in which oldest buds are formed at the tip of cadophore. These buds now develop into three type of zooids:

(i) Trophozooid or Gastrozooid

These zooids develop from the lateral buds of the cadophore and remain permanently attached to it. They are sterile zooids with a vegetative function, adding the entire colony as well as the parents oozooids in respiration and nutrition. The development of gastrozooid is rather simplified and restricted. Their dorsoventrally elongated body has a large funnel shaped branchial aperture and its musculature is vestigeal.

(ii) Phorozooids

The zooids develop from some of the median buds of cadophore, to which each one of them is attached by means of a short ventral stalk. Like the gastrozooid these zooids remain sterile but are not permanent sessile on the cadophore. These zooids detach from the cadophore of parent zooid and swim freely in the form of cork shaped bodies having *Doliolum* appearance with 8 muscular bands. The function of these zooids is to carry the third type of zooids (gonozooids) which develop from the buds that became attached to the stalk of these zooids previously when phorozooids are still attached to the cadophore.

(iii) Gonozooid

These are sexual zooids which attain their full development and maturity on the stalks of the free swimming phorozooids. The structure of the gonozooids resemble with the parent posterior but lack ventral stalk. When fully formed the gonozooids detach from the stalk of the parental posterior form and swim freely about and represent the solitary phase.

While buds of cadophore in a zooid are undergoing their respective development, the parent zooid present on nurse becomes greatly modified in structure, its branchial aperture, endostyle and alimentary canal, where as its muscular bands increase in thickness and nervous system becomes adapted to serve the function of a swimming organ of the entire colony.

The complicated life cycle of *Doliolum* thus existing regular alternation of generation between the sexually reproducing solitary phase and an asexually reproducing gregarine phase, the latter giving rise to temporary trimorphic colony, one type of which then develops into solitary individuals.

6

Rhabdopleura

Rhabdopleura was first seen by *Agassiz* in 1866, from the lands of the coasts of North Norvay. It was described by *Allmen* 1869 under the name *Rhabdopleura narmani*. It is said to be represented by three species: (i) *R. narmani* (2) *R. aunlate* from the coast of south Australia and New Zealand and (3) *R. striata* from Ceylon.

The coenicium consists of a branching tube creeping over and cemented to the substratum and giving at frequent intervals short free erect tube each housing a zooid. The substratum consists usually of the rocks, molluscan shells, Bryozoans, tunicates and like forms, but forms have also been found like sandy bottom (lying in sand). The colony is mostly of pale-brown colouration.

The creeping tube of the colony is flattened on its site of attachment and incorporates foreign particles. The erect tubes are cylindrical and transluscent. The creeping tube is divided into chambers by septa and each chamber typically leads into an erect tube. The zooid is partly housed in a chamber of the creeping tube and partly in the free erect tube, being attached to the septum. The erect tubes are made of successive rings and the creeping portion is also found of successive secretion laid on diagonal pieces.

In the attached wall of the creeping tube runs a blackcord called the black stolon, which connects all the zooids of the colony by transverse branches given off at each septum to the base of the zooid. As such Rhabdopleura is a true colony with zooids in organically continuity through the stolon.

External Feature

The zooid much resemble those of *Cephalodiscus*. They are small about 1mm in length excluding the stalk and are mostly dark brown in colour. The body is regionated into the (1) cephalic shield, (2) Collar, (3) trunk sac and stalk. The cephalic shield is of oval form with a central glandular area bounded posteriorly by the pigmented strip. It lacks however the lateral notches of *Cephalodiscus*. The collar very short ventrally being

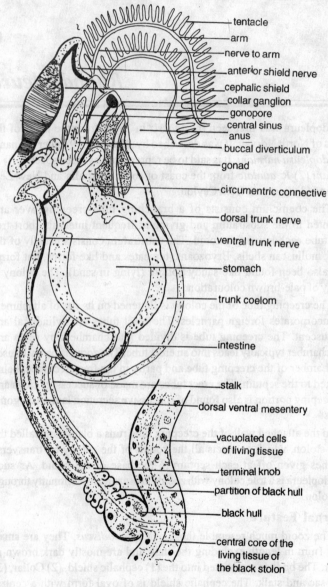

Fig. 6.1. Showing Anatomical features.

occupied entirely by the mouth. It is long dorsally where it bears a pair of arms guarded by a row of tentacles. On each side the arms curve backwards in the extended zooid and are held forward in the retracted form. From the base of the arm the oral lamella extends ventrally on each side, as a pronounced fold and the two folds meet behind the mouth. The right oral lamella is much larger and longer than the left.

The trunk sac is of elongated form. It bears the anus just behind the arm bases on the right side and a single gonopore on the same side just infront of anus. The stalk arises from the ventral side of the trunk sac and is attached by its end to a branch of the black stolon.

Internal Structure

It is similar to *Cephalodiscus*. The epidermis varies much in thickness and is ciliated, the ciliation is strongly developed on the tentacles, on the ventral surface of arms and in grooves on the oral side of the oral lamellae.

The cephalic shield resembles that of *Cephalodiscus*. The central area of its thick ventral epidermis is glandular and secretes the tube. The interior of the cephalic shield constitutes the protocoel and is crossed by radiating muscle fibres which extend from the shield collar septum to the ventral wall of the shield. The protocoel extends to the exterior by a pair of canals and pores, the latter striated interior to the arm bases.

The collar encloses a pair of coelomic cavities separated by the median dorsal mesentery, each leads dorsally into the arm coelom of the side which is filled with connective tissue and extends into the corresponding oral lamellae. It opens to the exterior by the collar canal and pore. The collar pores are minute and microscopic.

At the base of the dorsal collar ganglion, it gives a median anterior thickening in the cephalic shield, a posterior dorsal trunk nerve and a pair of circumentric connectives that meet ventrally to form a midventral trunk nerve, which continues between and along the ventral side of the stalk. There is a nerve from the ganglion along the dorsal side of each arm and two weak nerves along the ventral side. Nerve ganglionic cells occur in the anterior and posterior dorsal nerve trunk ending circumenteric connectives.

The trunk sac contains the usual pair of coelomic cavities and occupied by the digestive tract and gonads. The mouth is on the ventral side of the collar over hung by the posterior part of the cephalic shield. The thickened bulge of epidermis along the dorsal wall of mouth forms the upper lip and right and left oral lamellae form the lower boundary. The mouth is somewhat displaced to the left as the right oral lamellae are larger than the left. The short buccal tube gives off infront into the cephalic shield a well developed buccal diverticulum which lies in the shield collar septum supported by dorsal mesentery of the collar. The diverticulum may have no lumen or a continuous lumen in different species. The buccal tube is followed by pharynx provided with a pair of deep dorso-lateral grooves which represent the gill pouches that have not broken to the exterior. Behind the gill pouches the pharynx bases into the oesophagus which running through the collar trunk septum opens into the large sacciform stomach lined with epithelium. The stomach fills the intestine and hence the intestine leaving its posterior end makes, a forward curve along the right side of the stomach. The anus occupies as an elevation behind the arm bases. The shield collar and collar trunk septae are simple as there are no forwardly directed blind pouches. The ventral trunk mesentery is poorly developed in the trunk but is continued in the stalk dividing it into right and left halves.

Musculature

The sub epidermal layer of longitudinal muscle fibers is very weakly developed and is scarcely distinguishable from the peritoneum. The strongest musculature is in the stalk where two longitudinal ventral bundles arise which diminish in the trunk sac and continue to the oesophagus to the corresponding arms and another part encircled the buccal tube controlling the mouth opening. It also supplies the oral lamellae. The main mass of the oesophageal musculature extends forwards on either side of the buccal diverticulum attached to the shield collar septum and enters in the cephalic shield spreading in a fan like manner on its ventral side.

Circulatory System

The circulatory system resembles that of *Cephalodiscus*. The heart vesicle lies on the anterior tip of the buccal diverticulum and evolves the central sinus from it. The ventral shield sinus behind and below the buccal diverticulum bifurcates along the buccal tube and reunite on its ventral side to form the ventral trunk sinus which continues to the stalk. There is a dorsal trunk sinus which enters the central sinus from behind.

Glomerular tissue composed of stalked peritonial cells are present around the central sinus and ventral shield sinus, and it is less well developed than in Cephalodiscus.

Reproduction

Zooids are of separate sexes but the colonies are hermaphrodite. Most of the colonies are sterile and only some with male and female zooids are known. In the colony males are only 1/8 of the zooids and females are very scarce. The single gonad occupies the right metacoel and is elongated in male and rounded in female. In the testes only the proximal part produces sperms and the distal part forms the seminal vesicle. In the ripe stage the two parts may be separated by a constriction. The ovary contains one large yolky egg at a time. The eggs are discharged to the exterior but nothing is known about their embryonic development. The egg is said to have a free swimming *tornaria larva*.

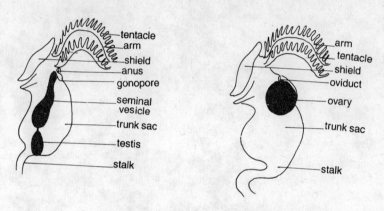

Fig. 6.2. Male and female sex organs.

The colony originates from a single sexually mature individual, from which one or more stolon grow out. Subsequent increase in the zooid number resulting in the colony formation by budding from the stolons. Only actively growing stolons which arise from the base of the preceeding young zooid branch and end into the buds. This young stolon is formed of an outer epidermis with a pair of cavities lined by peritonium and separated by mesentery, all continuous with the structures of the young zooid from which the stolon arises.

Active young stolon buds grow at the end after becoming young zooid. New stolons continue the process. The young bud is an evagination of the stolon. Soon two partitions are formed constituting the shield collar and collar trunk septa. The protosome enlarges into the cephalic shield (proboscis) and a subdivision of it forms the heart vesicle and the protocoel. The collar region is soon marked off and it produces the arm buds. Cells of peritonial origin form a rod between the two halves of mesentery. A stomodaeal invagination meets the rod and divides it into oesophagus and stomach. A proctodial invagination forms the intestine and joins the stomach.

After the bud has undergone considerable development partitions developed in each creeping tube separating each zooid from the other. The young zooid breaks through the upper wall and forms the free part of the tube by the secretion of successive rings.

Buds may not develop beyond the initial stage. It has been suggested that they are the dormant buds as an over-wintering device and will resume growth with the rise of temperature.

7

Cephalodiscus

Cephalodiscus was discovered by *Challanger* in 1876, but was mistaken to be compound Ascidian. *Harmer* 1887 described it as real marine as anomally of Enteropneusta.

It occurs in aggregation of several unconnected individuals or zooids arising by budding. The individuals secrete an encasement of unknown chemical nature called coenicium. The coenicium is often ornamented with filamentous projections which give it the appearance of a seed weed. It also includes foreign objects as sand grains, sponge spicules and fragments of molluscan shells. The collar is yellowish brown but the specimens are also orange, red or brown. This colour is generally lost later on preservation.

External Feature

Each zooid of the coenicium is a minute creature consisting of a clump body bearing feathery arms on the dorsal side of the neck and a long stalk which gives off buds. Despite the different appearance of coenicium the zooids of various species are practically identical. The body is divisible into three parts: (1) Protosome (2) Mesosome (3) Metasome.

The *protsome* or proboscis is a shield shaped or discform structure which is tilted to the ventral side for concealing the mouth. It is also called *buccal shield or cephalic shield.*

Viewed ventrally it is flat with more or less circular in its outline, intended laterally with a pair of notches. A curved red pigmented bond runs from one notch to the other, parallel to the posterior edge of the proboscis. Dorsally the central part of proboscis is directly continuous with mesosome.

Mesosome or collar is very much longer on the dorsal side than the ventral side. On its dorsal side it bears arms which are arranged bilaterally in two curved rows, composed of 5 to 9 arms each. All the arms of one row are fused basally. Each arm consists of a central stem bearing a groove on the ventral side and provided on each side with a fringe of 25 to 50 tentacles.

In some species the stem of arm terminates in a glandular knob which is adhesive. The number of tentacles is variable and may increase with the age. A fold of body wall called the *oral lamella* partly encircles the collar extending from the base of the most posterior arms around the ventral side. This serves to direct the food caught by the arms into the mouth.

Metasome or trunk is divisible into an anterior plumb part containing the recurved digestive tract, gonads and a posterior slender stalk for attachment. The plumb part bears the transversely elongated anus and two gonophores dorsally near the collar, and a pair of gill slits laterally. Just behind the collar, the stalk is hollow and muscular and it continues from the mid end of the trunk sac or from its side. Its length much exceeds than the rest of the animal. It's end is adhesive which helps the animal to attach to zone from which new zooids are constantly budded.

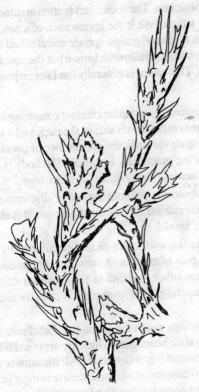

Fig. 7.1. A small portion of *Cephalodiscus*.

Anatomy

Body Wall. The body wall consists of the epidermis, nervous layer, basement membrane, sub epidermal musculature and peritonium. The epidermis is ciliated and glandular. The ciliation is better developed on the ventral side of arms and tentacles on oral lamella and on the dorsal side of the trunk in the viscinity of anus. The main glandular area lies on the ventral surface of the proboscis and is believed to secrete the coenicium. The base of epidermis is occupied by a nervous layer lined with basement membrane, which is sufficiently thickened on the dorsal side of the tentacles. It is followed by a layer of sub-epidermal longitudinal muscle fibres. The peritonium is partly transfered into muscle fibres and connective tissue but remains intact at places. A red or yellow curved pigmented strip bound the posterior border of the glandular area. Its function is unknown.

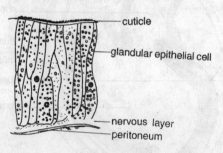

cuticle

glandular epithelial cell

nervous layer
peritoneum

Fig. 7.2. V.S. of Integument.

Nervous System

It consists of a fibrillar plexus at the base of the epidermis and above the basement membrane. This plexus thickens in the dorsal wall of the collar between the bases of the two arms as the collar ganglol, which consists of a fibrous mass containing ganglionic cells. The ganglionic cells are generally; absent from other parts of plexus except the mid ventral trunk nerve. From the ganglion several the so called nerves are given out which are merely thickening of these plexus. Into each arm is given off an arm nerve which runs along its dorsal side. In front, this plexus is continuous with the medial dorsal and a pair of latero-dorsal thickenings in the proboscis. From the hind end of the ganglion a short rather weak mid-dorsal trunk proceeds behind up to the arm.

The collar ganglion sends posteriorly a pair of prominent circumenteric connectives which proceeds to the ventral side along the collar trunk boundary behind the gill pores and unite on the ventral side of the trunk

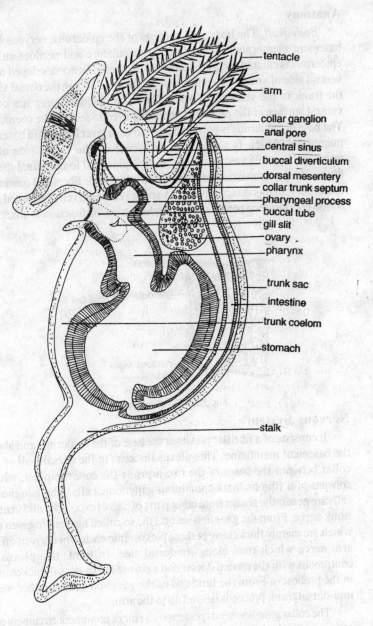

- tentacle
- arm
- collar ganglion
- anal pore
- central sinus
- buccal diverticulum
- dorsal mesentery
- collar trunk septum
- pharyngeal process
- buccal tube
- gill slit
- ovary
- pharynx
- trunk sac
- intestine
- trunk coelom
- stomach
- stalk

Fig. 7.3. Showing alimentary canal.

sac to form the mid ventral trunk nerve. It gives off 1 to 2 pairs of lateral trunk nerves continue on the ventral side of the stalk. The mid ventral trunk nerve may continue around the end of the stalk to its dorsal side and from there it may run forwards.

Coelom

It is divided into three compartments (1) the median protocoel (2) paired mesocoel and (3) paired metacoel. The protocoel, lies in the proboscis which is hollow except the posterior part, where its dorsal and ventral walls get fused. It is partly separated dorsally into a median dorsal and paired dorso-lateral pockets by the projection of the heart vesicle and associated structures. Each dorso-lateral pocket leads into a ciliated canal opening to the exterior by a small pore situated anterior to the base of the arm of its side. The protocoel is separated by the mesocoel by a transverse or oblique septum.

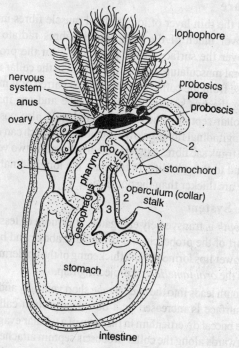

Fig. 7.4. Showing Coelomic cavities and gut.

The *mesocoel or collar* coal surrounds the buccal tube and is subdivided into the right and left halves by a dorsal and a ventral mesentery.

The dorsal mesentery is very thick and strongly developed while the ventral mesentery is thin. The mesocoel extends into the arms, tentacles and oral lamellae, The collar coelom also extends into the protocoel as a pair of blind pocket lined on either side of the heart vesicle. Each half of the collar coelom has a canal and a pore. The canal is circular in transverse section and opens on the side of the neck infront of the gill pore. The mesocoel is separated from the metacoel by a definite septum.

The *metacoel* or the *trunk coelom* is divided into the right and left halves by the dorsal and ventral mesenteries. It is almost completely filled by the alimentary canal and gonads. It sends a pair of ventral pockets into the collar coelom which extends up to the collar coelom. In the gonadial region a pair of lateral septa extends from the gonads to the dorsal mesentery. The metacoel extends into the stalk but lacks mesenteries. Its coelom is completely filled with muscles and connective tissues.

Musculature

Besides the thin layer of longitudinal muscle fibres underlying the epidermis over much of the body muscle fibres radiate through the protocoel, over the surface of the proboscis from the proboscis collar septa. The oral musculature is quite prominent in the collar region. These muscles arise from the collar trunk septum as paired oral muscles which sweep along the two sides of the buccal tube and are inserted on the proboscis collar septum. The trunk sac and stalk also possess a strong system of longitudinal fibres below the epidermis which can contract these parts. In the trunk sac fibres extend to the trunk wall in two ventral bundles which extend to the gill slits. In the stalk the longitudinal fibres on the ventral side are thicker than the dorsal side.

Digestive System

The *mouth* is transversely elongated. It is more or less concealed by the hind part of the proboscis and is bounded above and below by weak upper and lower lips formed by the thickening of the epidermis. Behind the lower lip is the *oral lamella* as a projecting flap.

The mouth leads into the *buccal tube* short ventrally and long dorsally, where its surface is increased by a dorsal projection called the *dorsal racess*. The buccal diverticulum in the form of a tubular evagination which extends forwards along the collar proboscis septum attached to the dorsal wall by the *dorsal collar mesentery*. The buccal diverticulum contains a single or a succession of cavities. The diverticulum is lined with epithelium often ciliated and mostly showing weak vacuolization.

The buccal tube passes into the *pharynx* through the collar trunk septum. The pharynx is lined with heavily ciliated and more or less glandular epithelium. A pair of gill passages perforates the dorso- lateral walls of the pharynx. They extend in the form of elongated passages lined with heavily vacuolated cells from the external slit like gill pore to the oval gill slits in the pharynx. In continuity with the gill passages lined by similar vacuolated cells are a pair of dorsolateral pharyngeal pockets which are regarded as *branchial sacs* as there are no tongue bars and skeletal supports in the pharynx as in Enteropneusta.

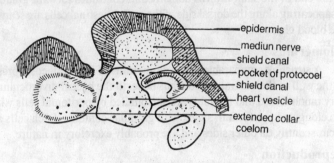

Fig. 7.5. T.S. of heart vesicle.

The pharynx continues behind as the oesophagus differentiated by the less ridged wall and absence of gland cells. The oesophagus opens into *stomach* which is expanded into a sac like form. It fills the greater part of the trunk sac (anterior part of trunk) and is lined with tall epithelium filled with secretory granules. The stomach is continued into the tubular *intestine* which curves dorsally and continues forward to the anus between the dorsal body wall and stomach. The intestinal epithelium is much less taller and contains secretory granules. Only a little beyond the stomach the terminal part of intestine expands into *rectum*.

Cephalodiscus feeds on minute organisms and particles captured by adhesive secretion of arms and conveyed by ciliary action along the grooves of arms to the oral lamella which directs them to the mouth.

Circulatory System

The circulatory system is mainly lacunar type and main channels lack definite walls. The *dorsal sinus* originates from the lacunar space. Over the stomach wall it runs forward as a well developed sinus above the oesophagus and pharynx, and is connected with another sinus surrounding each gonad. The dorsal sinus continues forward beneath the collar ganglion and terminates into the *central sinus* just infront of the buccal diverticulum.

This sinus is associated with the *contractile heart vesicle*. The central sinus is long tubular and almost is completely embraced by the heart vesicle. Muscle fibres occur on the outer surface of the central sinus and inner surface of the heart vesicle and the space between the two structures is crossed by radial muscle fibres. From the posterior end of the central sinus a large ventral sinus runs backwards beneath the buccal diverticulum and separates around the buccal tube as a pair of peribuccal channels. By the union of peribuccal channels the main *ventral sinus* originates. At the collar trunk septum, it proceeds behind along the ventral side of the stalk, at the end of the stalk it turns dorsally and continues forward gradually disappearing along the dorsal side of the stalk Intestinal cells are scanty in the blood channels.

Glomerulus

A structure comparable to the glomerulus of Enteropneusta present in the wall of the ventral shield sinus beneath the buccal diverticulum is very much folded and the folds are surrounded by peritonial cells which are elongated pyriform in shape with granular contents. Such cells also occur scantily on other sides and are probably excretory in nature.

Reproduction

Asexual. An outstanding feature is the formation of buds from its zooid near the posterior end of the stalk. Each zooid is found bearing 1 to 14 buds depending upon the space.

The buds originate as a pyriform outgrowth of the stalk epidermis with an extension of the stalk coelom and is divided by a dorso-ventral mesentery. Soon the distal end of the bud flattens and hardens to become the cephalic shield which is delimited behind by a groove showing the characteristic curved red pigment strip. Proximal to the shield, the bud enlarges on the trunk sac for sometime. The *cephalic shield* is disproportionately large but latter this disproportion is eliminated and the stalk also lengthens. On the dorsal surface first pair of arm appears as a pair of buds followed by other arms in an anterio posterior order. About this time the collar region becomes marked off from the trunk sac and the arms become the hollow extension of the collar region. In the interior of the bud, the coelom is sub-divided by cross partitions into an anterior *protocoel* and paired *mesocoel* and *metacoel*. The digestive tract is said to arise as an ectodermal invagination between the two leaves of the dorsoventral mesentery. Other workers indicate the origin of the digestive tract by the participation of an internal mass. The heart vesicle originates as a coelomic sac cut off from the protocoel and the buccal diverticulum as an evagination from the foregut. The gill passages are formed by evagination from the gut wall that meet the epidermis. The canals and pores of protocoel and mesocoel arise by ectodermal invagination. The gonads probably originate from the peritonial cells.

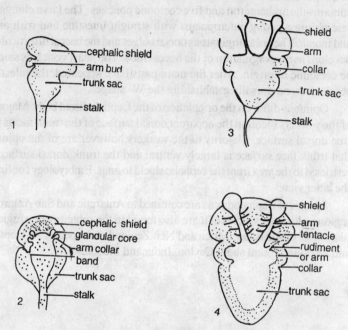

Fig. 7.6. Formation of bud in *Cephalodiscas*.

Sexual Reproduction. Sexes are separate but are not distinguishable. All the zooids of a coenicium may be of one sex or a mixture of two sexes. Even in a zooid one gonad may be male and other female in exceptional cases. In *Cephalodiscus hodgroni* the female zooids are however red with twelve arms and the male zooids are pale or brown with ten arms.

Breeding is probably seasonal occuring in the winter season i.e. from Oct. to January. In most of the cases the eggs are shed into the cavity of coenicium where they undergo development.

Development

The development is imperfectly known. The eggs are relatively large and very yolky but undergo *holoblastic* with nearly equal segmentation. The *blastula* is said to be hollow in some and solid in others. There is probably a regularly *embolic invagination*. Embryo develops a complete coat of cilia and escapes from the egg membrane. It develops the apical

sense organs with tuft of cilia on epidermal thickening. The ectodermal
part of the ventral surface of the larva thickens and becomes glandular. It
is said to be the primordial of the central glandular area of proboscis
developed preciously for the formation of coenicium. The anterior of larva
contains the archenteron and five coelomic pouches. The larva elongates
resembling a young enteropneust with straight intestine and with anus
and mouth. The arms originate as dorsal bulges and the buccal diverticulum
develops as an evagination of the buccal tube. The heart vesicle is said to
be coelomic in origin. After the main parts have appeared, the intestine
begins to bend dorsally establishing the W- shape.

Opinions differ on the orientation of the Cephalodiscid body. Majority
of the workers mention the apparent dorsal surface of the trunk sac as the
true dorsal surface. Majority of the workers however are of the opinion
that trunk face surface is largely ventral and the trunk dorsal surface is
restricted to the area from the cephalic shield to anus. Embryology confirms
the latter view.

Species of Cephalodiscus are confined to Antarctic and Sub Antarctic
regions, although species of it are also found in the subtemperate regions
like coasts of Australia, Africa and New Zealand. Sub species are tropical
and are found round about Ceylon, India and Indochina.

8

Pterobranchia and Its Affinities

Class *Pterobranchia* includes three living genera of which two genera, Cephalodiscus and Rhabdopleura are well known and third one is not so well known.

Members of this class are minutesized, true colonials with members in organic continuity, each enclosed in a secreted tube. They occur mainly in India and adjacent waters. Cephalodiscus has been found in wide range of localities in the Southern hemisphere, most of them are found in Japan and Korea. Rhabdopleura is reported from Scottland and S. Australia.

External Features

Cephalodiscus has an investment in the form of branching gelationous structure occupied by zooid. Each zooid is a minute creature consisting of clump body bearing feathers on the dorsal side of the neck and a long stalk. The body is divisible into three parts: Protosome, Mesosome and Metasome. The proboscis is a shield shaped lobe over hanging the mouth. The great number of tentacles are found over it. Its cavity communicates with the exterior by the two proboscis pores with the collar region. With the collar region is connected a series of usually 8 to 18 arms, each arm contains a prolongation of the collar.

Rhabdopleura

It occurs in colonies of zooids organically connected together by a creeping stolon and enclosed in, though not in organic continuity with a system of branching membranous tubes. The collar region bears a pair of hollow arms, each with a double row of slender tentacles. The whole is supported by a system of cuticular rods. The two collar pores lead into a ciliated canal with an internal funnel, and also there is a pair of proboscis pore. The zooids are of separate sexes, but the colony is hermaphrodite, although it is formed by budding.

Atubaria

It was described by *Sato* as recently as 1936. It resembles in general

165

appearance to *Cephalodiscus*, but lacks a protective investment. It is a free living and about 1.5 mm long. Adult possesses four pairs of tentaculate plumes or arms arranged in two rows. The collar region is short and thick and between collar and trunk there are dorsal genital and ventral growth apertures. The anal aperture is below the genital opening. Trunk is perforated by a pair of oblique branchial slits and tapers basally with no attachment disc, into a long tail like extremity.

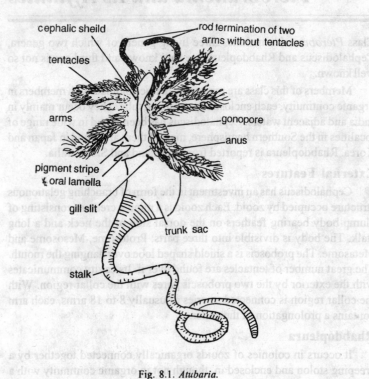

cephalic sheild

rod termination of two arms without tentacles

tentacles

arms

gonopore

anus

pigment stripe
& oral lamella

gill slit

trunk sac

stalk

Fig. 8.1. *Atubaria.*

Coelom

In *Cephalodiscus* the body cavity consists of an unpaired chamber in the proboscis, which opens to the exterior by a pair of pores. The cavity of the collar communicates with the exterior by a pair of ciliated collar pores. Behind the collar region on each side is a small area in which the body wall and that of pharynx are coealesent. This area is perforated by an opening, the gill pore. The dorso-ventral mesentry appears to persist completely in trunk region.

In other forms also same type of coelomic cavities occur i.e. unpaired proboscis coelom, paired colar and trunk coeloms.

Nervous System

A nerve strand, dorsal ganglion or collar cord containing nerve fibres and ganglionic cells are situated on the dorsal side of the collar deep in the epidermis. It is prolonged on to the dorsal surface of the proboscis and the dorsal surface of the arms. It is not hollow. On the ventral side of this nerve strand is a very slender cellular cord which is continuous behind with the epithelium of the pharynx. Above description agrees in all the forms of the class.

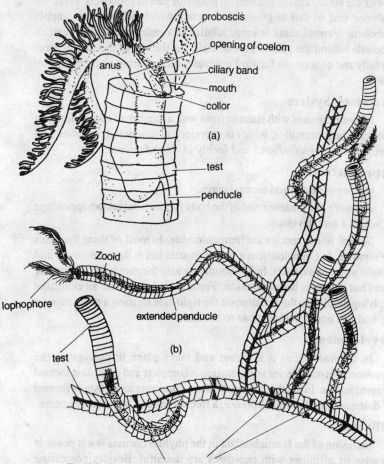

Fig. 8.2. External anatomy of pterobranchial hemichordata.

Digestive System

Alimentary canal consists of mouth cavity, pharynx, oesophagus, stomach and intestine which opens by posterior and dorsal anus. The alimentary canal bends on itself, so that the anal opening is situated not far from the mouth.

Circulatory System

It is a lacunar type and the main channels lack definite walls. The, dorsal vessel lies above the stomochord and ends anteriorly in a sinus, the dorsal sinus and heart. A closed cardiac sac is situated on the dorsal side of the sinus. This is situated on posterior part of proboscis. From the posterior end of this is given off a vessel which bifurcates to supply proboscis. Ventral sinus is long, tubular and embraced by the heart. It proceeds behind the ventral side of stalk. At the end of the stalk it turns dorsally and continuous forward gradually disappearing along the dorsal side.

Excretory System

It communicates with sinus in front with a number of vessels forming a plexus, the glomerulus, which is excretory in function. It is rather well developed in *Cephalodiscus* and feebly in *Rhabdopleura*.

Reproduction

Occurs in sexual and asexual ways.

Asexual : The posterior end of the body is drawn out into an appendage on which a bud develops.

Sexual. Some species are hermaphrodite. In most of them the sexes are separate. In Cephalodiscus a pair of ovaries lies in the trunk cavity and there is a pair of oviducts. In Rhabdopleura also the zooids are of separate sexes but colony is hermaphrodite. Testis is in the form of an elongated sac lying parallel to the intestine on the right side forming a projection on the body. It opens behind close to the anus.

Development

In *Cephalodiscus* it is direct and takes place in passage in the investment. In one species segmentation is complete and gastrula is formed by invagination. In another the segmentation is incomplete, gastrula formed by delamination. In *Rhabdopleura*, a free swimming larval stage occurs.

Affinities

Inclusion of the Hemichordata in the phylum craniata is not possible because its affinities with chordates are doubtful. Besides possessing pharyngeal gill clefts, they show no chordate characters.

1. There is no notochord but a structure called buccal diverticulum or stomochord which arises as an evagination of the buccal wall and not from the roof of the archenteron, as the notochord does. This buccal diverticulum differs from a notochord in its position, structure and mode of formation.

2. There is no central nervous system but only a cord of nervous tissue in the dorsal anterior part. This collar cord is joined by a nerve ring to a ventral nerve strand.

3. Body is not metamerically segmented but has three regions, a proboscis, a collar and a trunk. Both nervous and circulatory systems are of the invertebrate type.

   Their few chordate similarities are more than out weighed by important differences, hence, they are Hemichordata now placed as an independent phylum of Invertebrata.

4. They differ from *Balanoglossus* firstly in having the alimentary canal bent on itself so that the anal opening is situated not far from the mouth, and secondly in the presence of arms bearing tentacles arising from the collar.

   Pterobranchiate, moreover has only a single pair of gill pores, *Rhabdopleura* lacks such openings.

   Pterobranchiate and Rhabdopleura live in association or colonies secreting a common case or investment.

   Many features like nervous system, circulatory system are lost but not least the resemblance of Tornaria larva of some Rhabdopleura suggest their relationship with Echinodermata.

   Affinities with Graptolities were based on the lack of understanding of the structure of Graptolies. The arguments in favour of the affinity are secretion of chitinous tubes, structures of the tubes in consisting of successive half ring as Rhabdopleura, male theca of this group with the zooid tube of *Rhabdopleura*, and in the presence of a stolon connecting the zooids.

   The affinities with Phoronids are based on the segmentation of the body into three parts, epistome, prostome, lophophoral region, mesosome and trunk to metasome. It is however not confined by adult anatomy and embroyology.

   The affinities with Pogonophora lies in the presence of a single protocoel with a pair of ducts and pores to the exterior, presence of pericardial sac, location of gonads in the trunk, inter epidermal position of nervous system, strong septum of trunk, encruachment of the connective tissue and muscle fibres in coelom with the loss of definite peritonium as indication of incapient metamerism in the trunk region.

9

Asexual Reproduction in Tunicata

Introduction

Tunicates are interesting among chordata because they show an asexual method of reproduction called budding. They have long back known for their remarkable capacity for regeneration. Fundamentally these two processes being alike, it seems that budding is an explanation of regenerating capacity.

In general, structure the Tunicates have much in common but the differences in the sub division are rather important. In budding as it determines the exact nature of bud we have to deal basically with three different types.

Merosomatics types

(i) Zooids are divided into an elongated thorax and abdomen.

(ii) Holostometus forms no division in throax eg. *Perophora.*

(iii) Colonial forms like *Botrylls.*

Formation of Bud

Buds are usually produced as epidermal strobilization dividing the zooids by transverse constriction of epidermis. Thus girdle of epidermis cuts through gut, epicardium etc. till a completely separated bud is formed, the number of buds however differs from 2-8 depending upon size.

Generally there is an elongation of region where the buds are formed. Budding here follows a process of extensive and active growth. The constriction appears successively from anterior to posterior side when a definite interval is over and after the appearance of previous constriction. This is simplest of budding. A detailed account in some families with a more complex method are as follows -

BUDDING IN VARIOUS FAMILIES

Family : Diazonidae

1. Merostomeous forms (body divided into head, thorax, abdomen, etc.).

2. Thorax undergoes regression. The siphons are closed. As a result of this thorax questionally condenses.

3. Due to autolysis thorax and oesophagus being dissolved.

4. During this certain cells are loaded with nutritive materials. Trophocytes and thesocytes descend into abdominal portion.

5. Epidermal constriction appears like beads.

6. Regeneration of the organ from the buds depends on the constriction of the latter epidermis.

Diazonia: The regression is greater and only post abdomen with heart and gonads remain new individuals or bud individuals.

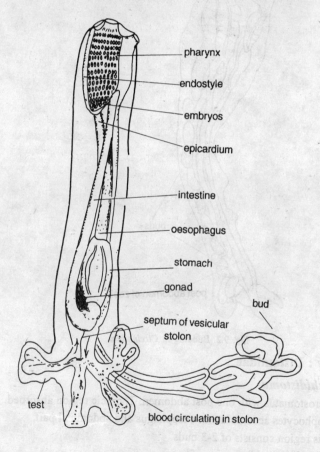

Fig. 9.1. Budding in *Clavelina*.

Family : Syneicidae

1. *Morehellium* colonial zooids merosomates and post abdomen ends are smaller than *Diazonia*.
2. Anterior part degrated, post part being filled with Archeocytes of post abdomen.
3. Post abdomen consists of three to four buds.
4. Formating tissue and epicardium and hence bud has very few adult structures. It is more recognization than regeneration.

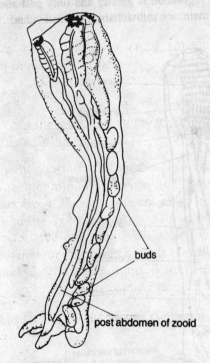

buds

post abdomen of zooid

Fig. 9.2. Budding in *Circinalium*.

Family : Distomidae

A: *Archidistoma*

1. Merostomatus with one post abdomen. Thoracic region absorbed.
2. Trophocytes accumulate in oesophagus and abdominal part.
3. This region consists of 2-3 buds.
4. Epicardium and formation of tissue.

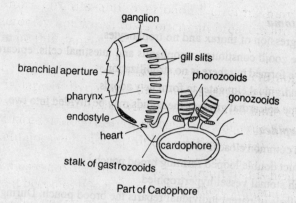

Part of Cadophore

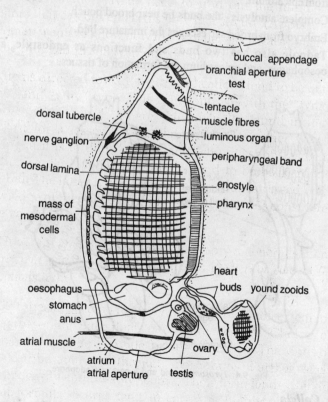

Fig. 9.3. *Pyrosoma zooid* and a part of Cadophore.

B: *Endistoma*

1. No regression of thorax and no trophocytes.
2. Whole zooid constitutes oesophagus and intestinal cells, epicardial groove formed but there is no strobilization.
3. The individual elongates to form new zooids.
4. In some epicardial grooves the zooids may be divided into two.

C: *Distapidea*

1. Has a common cloacal cavity.
2. Oviduct double looped forming brood pouch.
3. Pouch stomal vessel hypertrophied.
4. Autolysis of parent individual reparts the brood pouch. During this two small masses develop in the region of oesophagus and pharynx from epicardium.
5. Complete autolysis - the buds lie near brood pouch.
6. Embryo from brood sac escapes the immature bud.
7. Tadpole also has two buds and functions as endostyle, and oesophagus, and epicardium are formation of tissues.

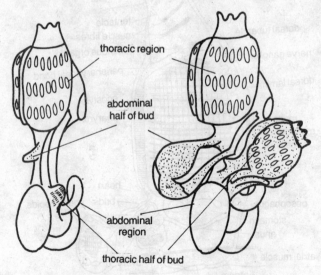

Fig. 9.4. *Tyrosoma* zooid and a part of Cadophore.

D. *Collela*

1. Pedunculata and colonial species.

2. Peduncle formed from stomach.
3. Individuals degenerate and buds arise at the junction of colony and stolon.
4. Stolonic vessels divided into two by a mesenchymatous septum. Cells proliferate from this and represent formative tissue.

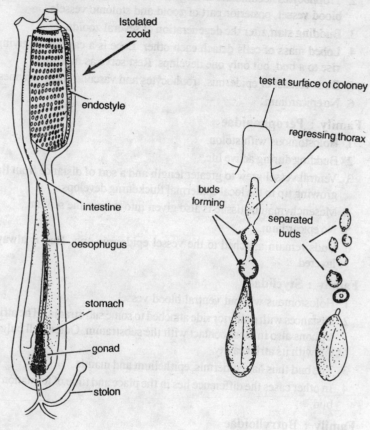

Fig. 9.5. Budding in *Diazona*.

Family : Didaminadae

1. Epidermal out growth appears in oesophageal region, one anterior and one posterior.
2. Epidermal pouches now grow into it.
3. These out growths are partial buds. The anterior one develops abdomen and posterior one thorax.

4. Merostomatus with a very short abdomen and without a posterior abdomen.

Family : Calvellinae

1. Merostomatus, no posterior abdomen, stolonic vessels large.
2. Trophocytes accumulate in large number and pass into body cavity, blood vessel, posterior part of zooid and stolonic vessels.
3. Budding start after the degeneration of several zooids.
4. Lobed mass of cells detach each other. Lobe is a capsule of giving rise to a bud, but only one develops. Rest serve as nutrition.
5. Buds consist of epidermis, trophocytes and vascular mesenchymes.
6. No epicardium.

Family : Perophonidae

1. Holostomous with stolon.
2. Budding during active life.
3. Ventral vessel grew to greater length and a sort of distance from the growing tip to the local epidermal thickening develops.
4. Mesenchymatous tissue is also given into it from the septum.
5. No epicardium.
6. Buds remain attached to the vessel epidermis only. Bud is always layered.

Family : Styclidae

1. Holostomous without ventral blood vessel.
2. Distances with posterior side attached to some sub-stratum. The atrial siphons also in close contact with the substratum. Outer wall bulges out with its atrial cavity.
3. The bud thus has epidermis, epithelium and mantle.
4. In other cases the difference lies in the place and time of formation of bud.

Family : Botrylloidae

One bud arise from the right side of the ova zooid and develops fully in three days. The older individuals degenerate and bud new ones. But before they are fully formed they also bud on their right sides.

BUDDING IN THALACEA

1. The budding stolon is an epidermal out growth from body wall of the base of the endostyle.
2. The inner contents are the extensions of the endostyle and are

peripharyngeal in origin.

3. Budding starts with epidermis as in Ascidians.

4. The details of budding differ as far as the length of the stolons.

5. No budding in appendicularia.

Regression

1. A more or less orderly process of reproduction without involving the death of colony.

2. It results in the compact masses of tissue reminants in ectodermal envelops.

3. The process is known from of colonial Ascidians only.

4. It generally takes place in adverse conditions.

Bud Maintenance

Buds once established require nutrition for the growth untill able to feed.

(a) Heavily loaded buds with reserve food. Ex = *Diazonia, Archidistoma.*

(b) Buds live in external nutritive medium.

(c) Modification of maintaining organic continuity with parent. Ex = *Salpa, Pyrosoma.*

(d) Establishing a new connection Ex =*Botryllus.*

Constitution of Bud

All buds have an outer layer of epidermis which is one layered in thickness.

The inner constituents, however, differ.

1. Epidermis and epicardium and section of intestine and dorsal cord.

2. Epidermis and epicardium and dorsal cord.

3. Epidermis and Endostyle + Mesenchyme.

Examples - *Salpa, Doliolum.*

Tissue Patches

Epidermis which shows tunicin secretion and is beyond embryonic ectodermal stage gives epidermis only.

The thalacian epidermis is however immature and is multipotent and gives neural ganglion and glands unlike other buds epidermis and are incapable of producing these structures.

Intestinal epidermis gives rise to intestine and dorsal cord tissue. neural gland and neural ganglion.

10

Endocrine Glands of the Protochordata

Protochordates are the primitive chordates and are of exceptional interest, because they combine certain features of vertebrate organisation with other characteristics which provide something of a link with the Echinodermata, the group of invertebrates to which the vertebrates are now thought to be most closely related. Thus, we may reasonably expect that endocrinological investigations of the group will extend our understanding of the origin, organisation and functioning of vertebrate hormonal systems.

The best-known protochordates are the Cephalochordata, represented by *Amphioxus,* and the Urochordata (Tunicata), including the sessile ascidians (sea-squirts) and various pelagic forms such as the *Salps*. All of these are filter feeders, and they resemble each other in the possession of a large filtering pharynx, along the floor of which runs a groove or channel, the *endostyle*. This organ is provided with pairs of longitudinal glandular tracts, and it is generally held that it contributes to the mucus-like secretions with which the animals trap small particles of food material. An organ closely resembling it, and clearly homologous with it, is found in the ammocoete larva of the lamprey, the most primitive surviving vertebrate. It has long been known that at the metamorphosis of this larva a part of the endostyle is transformed into the thyroid gland, and it has been established by *Gorbman* and *Creaser* (1942), by *Leloup* and *Berg* (1954), and by *Leloup* (1955) that even in the larva the endostyle is trapping and binding iodine and is thereby forming *monoiodotyrosine*, *di-iodotyrosine*, *thyroxine*, and probably *tri-iodothyronine*.

As regards *Amphioxus, Thoms* (1956) has shown that the endostyle of this animal does, in fact, contain organically bound iodine, demonstrable in auto-radiographs, prepared from animals which has been immersed in sea water containing I^{131}. *Thomas* inclined to ascribe some at least of the iodine binding in the endostyle to the more dorsal of the two pairs of glandular tracts. *Barrington* (1958), however, made it clear that the centre

178

of iodination lies at, or near to, the surface of a group of cells lying immediately above these tracts; the latter do not themselves appear to be involved in iodination, and in this respect the situation resembles that already established for the endostyle of the ammocoete larva.

It has further been shown that in *Amphioxus* the cell concerned produce a clearly defined secretion; this may reasonably be regarded as providing the molecular basis for the binding process and it is thus of obvious interest to compare it with thyroglobulin. Like the latter, it is strongly PAS-positive, but certain other tests reveal considerable differences (*Barrington*, 1958). The significance of these is not easy to assess, owing to the lack of precise information as to the chemical composition of so-called *muco-substances*. It can be said, however, that epithelial mucins which are characteristic of alimentary tracts, and which we should reasonably expect to find in the pharynx of *Amphioxus,* have as a major component the carbohydrate polymers known as acid mucopolysaccharides (*Pearse*, 1954) or, as *Kent* and *Whitehouse* (1955) would prefer, as *aminopolysaccharides*, these being carbohydrates which contain the 2-aminosugars glucosamine and galactosamine. Secretions of this type react positively with mucicarmine and with alcian blue, and show the characteristic red colour of gamma metachromasia with toluidine blue.

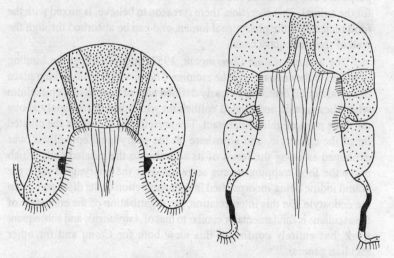

Fig. 10.1. Diagrams of the endostyles of *Ciona* and *Amphioxus* to show the relationships of the iodination centers to the other regions of the organs. In both animals these centers (black) lie near the lip of the endostyle and immediately above the glandular tracts.

The thyroglobulin of thyroid colloid, being a glycoprotein, is negative to these three tests, but the secretion of the iodine-binding cells of the *Amphioxus* endostyle is positive. This may well mean that in the later animal one in which the process is associated with the presence of an alimentary muco-substance. It has been suggested that the iodine is bound to a carbohydrate polymer. The position seems to be that aminopolysaccharides are often, and perhaps always (*Kent* and *Whitehouse*, 1955; *Leblond et.al.*, 1957), associated loosely with some protein; it is presumably to the latter that binding takes place, and the possibility that it is itself a thyroglobulin-like substance is not excluded by these tests. The point of interest is that iodine binding seems here to be evolving out of an essentially alimentary secretory process.

A further important conclusion which can be drawn from *Amphioxus* result from the clearly observable fact that cells other than those associated with iodine binding react positively to the tests for epithelial mucins, notably a group of cells lying at the base of the groove. No bound iodine has been found to be associated with these, however, and we can thus conclude that the binding is not a random result of any generalised property of mucins, but is a specialised property of one particular group of cells. From this it would seem to follow that the binding is a biochemically purposive act, giving rise to a secretion which is biochemically significant for the animal. This secretion, there is reason to believe, is mixed with the food material in the pharyngeal lumen, and can be absorbed through the wall of the alimentary canal.

The ascidian *Ciona* (*Barrington*, 1957) suggested that the binding of iodine in the endostyle of the ascidian *Cliona* was actually taking place in an iodination centre in a clearly defined area of nonciliated epithelium which lies area of nonciliated epithelium which lies immediately above the three pairs of galandular tract. The presence of iodine on the ciliated lip of the endostyle, and elsewhere on the pharyngeal epithelium, was explained as being the result of its adhesion to the ciliated cells which move the food-trapping mucus secretion over the pharyngeal wall, the bound iodine being incorporated into this secretion on its discharge from the endostyle. On this interpretation, the organisation of the endostyle of the ascidians is fundamentally similar to that of *Amphioxus,* and subsequent work, has entirely confirmed this view both for *Ciona* and for other ascidian genera.

Good examples of the latter are provided by *Dendrodoa* and *Botryllus,* which, as members of the order Pleurogona, have a more specialised organisation than *Ciona* and are regarded by the systematist as widely separated from it (*Berrill*, 1950). In *Dendrodoa* a region involved in the synthesis is clearly defined, although it is less extended than in *Ciona;* its cell contain PAS-positive material, and in auto-radiographs bound iodine is associated with them as well as the ciliated lip of the endostyle. *Botryllus* is particularly striking, for in this well-known colonial form the individual zooids are minute in size, ranging up to only 4 mm in length, as compared with the 25 mm of *Dendrodoa* or 12 cm or more of *Ciona*. Despite this, the same regions are distinguishable in the endostyle, and clear autograph images indicate an iodination centre in the upper part of endostyle, whereas elsewhere, on the ciliated lip and over the pharyngeal wall, the signs of bound iodine are irregular and may be quite inconspicuous.

At present the nature of the secretion of the iodine-binding cells is less easily definable in the ascidians than it is in *Amphioxus,* and individual genera may prove to vary in this respect. In *Ciona,* it bears some resemblance to the secretion of the corresponding cells of the endostyle of the ammocoete larva. In *Dendrodoa* it is PAS-positive but probably differs from the corresponding secretion in *Amphioxus* in being negative to alcian blue and to mucicarmine. In *Botryllus* PAS-positive droplets are sometimes distinguishable, but often there is no sign of secretion at all, probably, in part, because of the very small size of the cells and the difficulty of securing satisfactory fixation of them. This matter is still under investigation, but in the meantime it may be well to emphasize that the adult ascidians are probably not on the direct line of ascent to

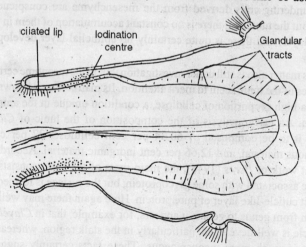

Fig. 10.2. Diagram of an autoradiograph of a transverse section of the endostyle of *Botryllus*.

vertebrates, and are presumbly much less closely related to the latter than is *Amphioxus*. Current theory derives the vertebrates, and also *Amphioxus* itself, by neoteny from the ascidian larval stage (*Berrill*, 1955), although the further possibility that both *Amphioxus* and the *Tunicata* may have arisen independently from the third protochordate Subphylum, the Hemichordata, cannot be excluded (*Bone*, 1958). On either view it would seem that adult tunicates must have pursued their own independent specialisations, which might in some cases be expected to parallel those of vertebrates and in others to diverge from them.

An important result of these studies on tunicates has been the demonstration of the presence of bound iodine in other parts of their bodies. There have been earlier reports of its occurence in the stolonic septa of *Perophora annectens* (*Gorbman*, 1941), and in the canals connecting the zooids of *Botryllus* (*Gorbman et. al.*, 1954). However, its accumulation in large quantities in the tunic has also been observed. This tunic is a tough protective coat which is secreted over the body and was shown by *Cameron* (1914) to be very rich in iodine. Auto-radiographs show that some at least of this iodine is organically bound and that it is actually very much more conspicuous here than it is in the endostyle. The main concentration is found to be in a narrow zone at the extreme surface, an important fact that at once brings into focus a striking contrast with the situation obtaining in the endostyle, for there is no evidence that the binding of iodine in the tunic is related to any particular groups of cells. It is true that woundering cells derived from the mesenchyme are conspicuous throughout the tunic, but there is no constant accumulation of them in the surface layer, and there is quite certainly no epithelial layer developed there.

This matter also is still under investigation, but in the meantime certain properties of the tunic seem to merit attention. Its matrix is well known to contain a high proportion of cellulose, a condition unique in the animal kingdom. An early analysis of the composition of the tunic of *Ciona* showed it to be composed of 60.34 per cent cellulose, 27 per cent nitrogenous material, and 12.66 per cent inorganic material. According to recent work of *Peres* (1948), the main mass of the tunic consists of cellulose associated with some glycoprotein, but the surface is formed of a distinct cuticle-like layer of pure protein. Here again there may well be variation from genus to genus; it appears, for example, that in *Clavelina* the cuticle is well-developed, particularly in the stalk region, whereas in *Ciona* it is much more inconspicuous. These facts certainly suggest, however, that we are dealing here with the phenomenon which has been shown to characterise a wide range of invertebrates, the association of iodine binding with the laying down of exoskeletal scleroproteins (*Gorbman*, 1955).

At this stage of the analysis it is clearly necessary to inquire as to the nature of the iodinated products which arise in the protochordates, for this has an obvious bearing on the question as to how far we are here dealing with an hormonal situation. As far as *Amphioxus* is concerned, the only positive evidence comes from the work of *Sembart* (1953), who implanted 40 dried endostyles into one axolotl and 65 into another, and thereby produced metamorphic reduction of the fins and gills. Since control implants of muscle had at most only slight effects, this was regarded as giving some indication of the presence of thyroid hormone in the endostyle.

The activity of aqueous extracts of the tunic is weak, but treatment of the tissue with *N* NaOH at 50°C for 5 hours gives extracts of very much higher activity, a result which provides some support for the view, suggested above, that the bound iodine is associated with structural proteins. The radioactivity of aqueous extracts of the endostyle is very low, as is to be expected from the weak auto-radiographs given by this organ, but the same radio-chromatographic procedure has given good evidence for the presence in these extracts of diiodotyrosine, and it is highly probable that at least thyroxine is also present.

Perhaps at this point one might conveniently summarise the conclusions which seem to emerge from this review, always bearing in mind that these particular investigations are still in progress, and that the arguments should at this stage be regarded as primarily a reasoned directive for further research. As far as the endostyle is concerned, iodine binding is already established in it at the protochrodate level of evolution, and it is established in a localised region of the organ in such a manner as to suggest that it is biochemically purposive and not a product of random iodine uptake. The cells concerned produce a secretion which, at least in *Amphioxus,* is iodinated at or near to the cell surface, as it apparently is in the cells of the thyroid gland of vertebrates. There is presumably little storage, and the iodinated secretion is discharged and becomes mixed with food cords, probably to be absorbed through the epithelium of the alimentary canal. It is highly probable that this iodine binding is indicative of an essentially thyroidal hiosynthesis, and one may surmise that the replacement of the mucin-like secretion of *Amphioxus* by thyroglobulin may have provided a more efficient molecular basis for this purpose and for the storage of its products. It is interesting in this connection to note that *Hooghwinkel et. al.* 1954) have interpreted thyroglobulin as a firm compound of mucopolysaccharide and protein, although as *Gross* (1957) has pointed out, their results seems to conform also to the usual view that it is a glycoprotein. One may further surmise that this cytochemical evolution may well have been determined by the shortage of iodine which the chordates would have encountered when they migrated from marine to freshwater habitats, and this may also account for what seems to be a greater area of iodinating epithelium in the endostyle of the ammocoete larva as compared with that of the protochordates. Here, then, would seem to be an ecological adaptation, analogous to those which have been considered elsewhere in this symposium, but operating on a geological time scale.

As regards the tunic, the association of bound iodine with cuticular structures is by no means novel, for it has been recorded in annelids, arthropods, and molluscs. This association may well be a biological accident, with the degree of fixation and the yield of thyroxine being determined by the disposition of the tyrosine residues in scleroprotein molecules (*Wheeler*, 1950; Roche and *Michel* 1951), and it has been plausibly argued (*Gorbman*, 1955) that the thyroid gland might have evolved as a consequence of the ancestors of vertebrates becoming biochemically dependent on iodinated amino acids which were initially made available to them by such accidental means. It would be premature to developed this argument far in our present state of knowledge, but it is quite clear that conditions in the tunicates lend some support to it. Their tunic is often richly provided both with wandering mesenchyme cells and with blood vessels, so that it is by no means unlikely that some of its iodinated products might be released and transported through the body, and thus available for utilization. Further, and perhaps more important, the tunic is not a passive tissue (*Berrill*, 1950), but is constantly being secreted by the epidermis and lost from the surface, so that there would seem to be rather a good possibility of these ciliary feeding animals ingesting, and subsequently digesting, some of their own iodinated products, the more so in that they are often gregarious or colonial in habit. It is surely far from fantastic to suggest that in some such way tunicates might have become biochemically dependent upon these iodinated products at an early stage of their evolution; the iodinating properties of the endostyle might have arisen thereafter as an adaptation for the secretion of these substances in a form more readily available and in a position from which they could more easily be assimilated.

Other aspects, and particularly those related to reproduction, have been reviewed by *Dodd* (1955), who has drawn attention to the uncertainly of the evidence which has from time to time been held to establish the homology of the neural gland of the Tunicata with the pituitary of vertebrates. In the year 1958, *Dodd* has now satisfied himself that no gonadotrophin, assayable by mouse or male toad methods, exists in the neural complex of breeding *Ciona,* nor is there any convincing evidence for the presence of vasopressin or of melanophore-expanding hormone. He certainly finds some support for the contention of earlier workers that an oxytocic substance is present, but the significance of this is quite obscure, for he has been able to show that its properties are very different from those of mammalian oxytocin whereas a very similar substance can be extracted from various parts of the bodies of starfish and lungworms. Here, then, is a field in which recent work, in complete contrast to that on the endostyle, has failed to substantiate earlier views.

At the present time the clearest positive evidence as to the function of the neural gland of tunicates is that it has powers of phagocytosis (*Peres*, 1943) and that it is capable of taking up finely divided particles which have entered the inhalent siphon in incurrent stream of water (*Godeaux*, 1953). It seems well to emphasize once again in this connection that if vertebrates are derived from ascidians it is from their larvae and not from the adults, and that although the larvae possess an endostyle they certainly do not possess a neural gland, although the neotenous appendicularians are said to have a well-developed ciliated tubercle, this being the structure on which the duct of the gland opens in the adults of the other groups. It may, then, be more prudent to think of the neural gland not so much as a forerunner of the pituitary, but as an independent specialisation of the Tunicata, although, of course, it might still be the expression of some genetic potentiality common to all the lower chordates.

Brambell and *Cole* (1939) have suggested that some such common potentiality for the production by invagination of an anterior pit-like organ may explain the development of the ciliated organ which they discovered at the base of the proboscis of the Enteropneusta. It might also account for the existence in *Amphioxus* of Hatschek's pit, for there are excellent morphological and embryological grounds for homologising it with the adenohypophysis, as *Goodrich* (1917) first demonstrated. Its function has often been said to be the secretion of mucus to aid in the trapping of food, but its cell structure is so elaborate that it is difficult to feel satisfied with such a simple interpretation. It is said to have no nerve supply, but some of its cells have long-drawn-out distal ends which project into the lumen of the pit, and one wonders whether they may not be sensitive to substances in the water current passing over them. Without wishing to indulge in too easy-going speculation, one cannot but wonder whether the evolutionary history of this organ may not have some analogy with the story of the endostyle outlined above. Just as a mucus-secreting pharyngeal organ, with powers of iodination, seems to have evolved into a glycoprotein-secreting gland, so perhaps might a mucus-secreting stomodaeal pit, sensitive to passing subsstances, have evolved into another glycoprotein-secreting gland, sensitive to materials reaching it in the blood. Here at least is an obvious field for further investigation.

Where, it may be asked, is one then to look for the homologue of the neurohypophysis? There is, in fact, in the floor of the cerebral vesicle of *Amphioxus* a group of peculiar cells referred to by earlier workers as an infundibular organ. *Olsson* and *Wingstrand* (1954) have shown that these are nerve cells containing Gomori-positive granules, although since they appear to secrete a Reissner's fibre they have something in common with the subcommissural organ of vertebrates, which is composed of ependymal cell secreting a Gomori-positive material. *Franz* (1923) believed that they were light-sensitive. According to his interpretation, they respond to shadows cast upon them by the so-called "eye-spot" which is situated in front of them, in the anterior wall of the cerebral vesicle, and he believed them to be an essential element in the orientation of the animal to light and shade. This particular problem has been reviewed in later publications by *Olsson* (1958), and further study will be needed before we can hope to resolve it or, indeed, any of other problems.

Index